Task
MATHS
3

BARBARA BALL & DEREK BALL

Nelson

Thomas Nelson and Sons Ltd
Nelson House Mayfield Road
Walton-on-Thames Surrey
KT12 5PL UK

58 Albany Street
Edinburgh
EH1 3QR UK

Nelson Blackie
Wester Cleddens Road
Bishopbriggs
Glasgow
G64 2NZ UK

Thomas Nelson (Hong Kong) Ltd
Toppan Building 10/F
22a Westlands Road
Quarry Bay Hong Kong

Thomas Nelson Australia
102 Dodds Street
South Melbourne
Victoria 3205 Australia

Nelson Canada
1120 Birchmount Road
Scarborough Ontario
MIK 5G4 Canada

Published by Thomas Nelson and Sons Ltd 1994

ISBN 0-17-431166-4
NPN 9 8 7 6 5 4 3 2 1

Printed in Spain

Acknowledgements

The authors are grateful to all those teachers and students who have helped
by trialling the material in this book. They value, in particular, the frequent
and most helpful advice they received from John Mabbs, Sue Pope, Ian
Robinson and Philip Whiffing. They also acknowledge the help of
St. Martin's Record Shop, Leicester.

They would also like to thank the students of Longslade Community College
and Susan Lander and the children of Gaddesby County Primary School.

Acknowledgement is due to the following for the use of data:
Anthropometrics by Stephen Pheasant, published by and available from the
British Standards, Linford Wood, Milton Keynes, MK14 6LE.
BPI

The majority of the photographs were supplied by David Bamber.

ABOUT THIS BOOK

This book is organised into tasks, not into mathematical topics as most mathematics books are. There are seventeen tasks in this book. While working on any one of these tasks you will meet a number of different mathematical topics.

Each task is divided into a number of activities which develop the task. The activities also help to develop your knowledge, skills and understanding of mathematics. Sometimes there are information boxes to explain mathematical words, ideas or techniques.

There are six sections of review exercises in this book. These exercises contain questions which enable you to consolidate particular mathematical topics.

Throughout this book it is assumed that you have a calculator available whenever you need it (although there are one or two activities to do without a calculator). On many pages there is a picture of a computer. This indicates that a computer, or sometimes a graphical or programmable calculator, would be very useful for working on a particular activity.

Many of the questions in this book are marked with yellow squares. These are somewhat harder than the unmarked questions. Some are marked with blue squares. These are harder still.

At various points in this book you will find a diamond shape in the margin. Inside this diamond shape is a review exercise code and a page number. This tells you that you can turn to the review exercise shown for more practice on the techniques introduced in the task. Each diamond is colour coded white, yellow or blue to show how difficult the review exercise is.

CONTENTS

POLYGON RINGS

You might find ATM MATS useful for this task.

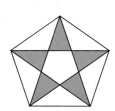
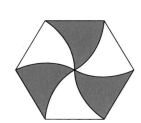
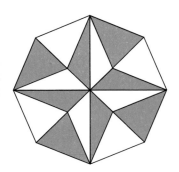

RINGS OF PENTAGONS

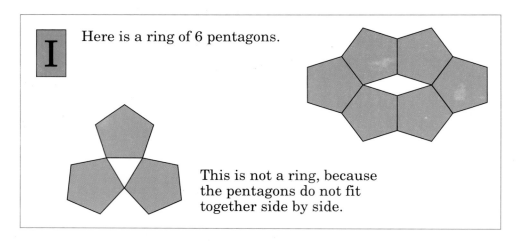

I Here is a ring of 6 pentagons.

This is not a ring, because the pentagons do not fit together side by side.

1 Make some rings of pentagons. Answer these questions about each of your rings.

   (*a*) How many pentagons are there in the ring?

   (*b*) Describe the symmetry of the ring.

   (*c*) Name the shape of the space inside the ring.

      Can the space inside a ring of pentagons be a regular shape?

2 Can you make *different* rings with the same number of pentagons?

You could use the computer program *Tiling* for any of these activities.

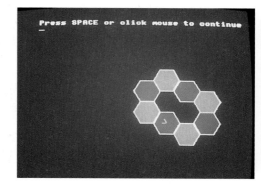

RINGS OF HEXAGONS

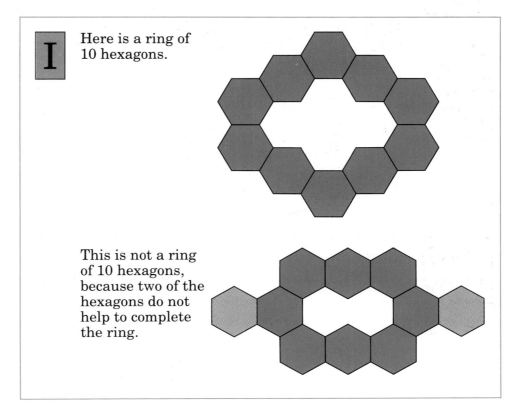

I Here is a ring of 10 hexagons.

This is not a ring of 10 hexagons, because two of the hexagons do not help to complete the ring.

1 Make some rings of hexagons. Answer these questions about each of your rings.

(a) How many hexagons are there in the ring?

(b) Describe the symmetry of the ring.

(c) Name the shape of the space inside the ring.

(d) Find the area of the space inside the ring.

Can the space inside a ring of hexagons be a regular shape?

2 Can you make *different* rings with the same number of hexagons?

> You might find the resource sheet *Hexagons* useful for this activity.

RINGS OF POLYGONS

Make some rings of polygons. Think of some problems to solve about polygon rings.

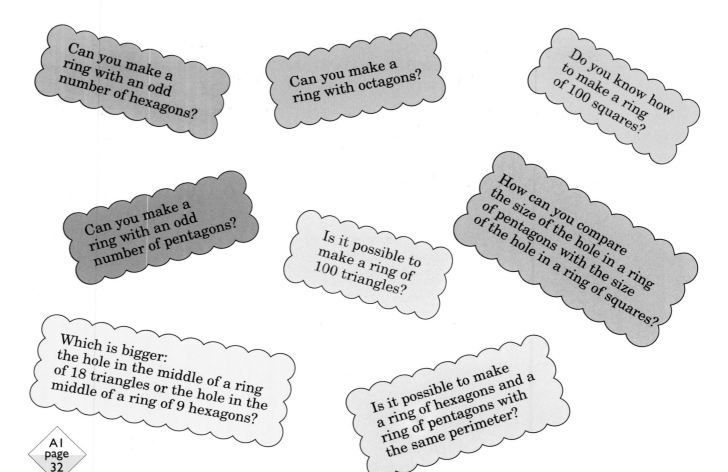

Can you make a ring with an odd number of hexagons?

Can you make a ring with octagons?

Do you know how to make a ring of 100 squares?

Can you make a ring with an odd number of pentagons?

Is it possible to make a ring of 100 triangles?

How can you compare the size of the hole in a ring of pentagons with the size of the hole in a ring of squares?

Which is bigger: the hole in the middle of a ring of 18 triangles or the hole in the middle of a ring of 9 hexagons?

Is it possible to make a ring of hexagons and a ring of pentagons with the same perimeter?

A1 page 32

CRAWLING AROUND THE RING

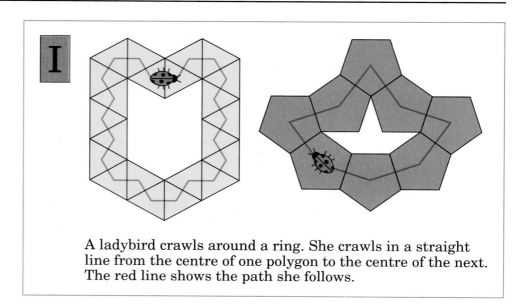

I

A ladybird crawls around a ring. She crawls in a straight line from the centre of one polygon to the centre of the next. The red line shows the path she follows.

1 (*a*) When the ladybird crawls around the ring of triangles in the box opposite, how many times does her path change direction?

   (*b*) How many times does she turn right?

   (*c*) How many times does she turn left?

   (*d*) Through what angle does she turn each time?

2 Repeat question 1 for the ring of pentagons in the box opposite.

3 Here are some more rings. Answer question 1 for each of these rings.

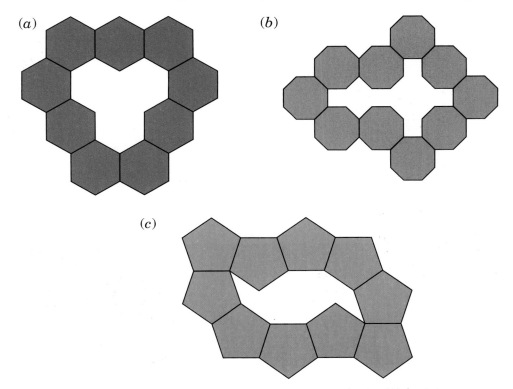

(*a*)

(*b*)

(*c*)

4 Answer question 1 for some rings of your own.

5 Can you help solve these problems?

You might be able to use the idea of the crawling ladybird to prove some imposs-ibilities about rings.

'I can't find a pentagon ring with an odd number of pentagons.'

'I can't find an octagon ring with an odd number of octagons.'

MIXED RINGS

 Here is a ring of pentagons and hexagons.

1 (a) What is the symmetry of the ring in the box above?

(b) Describe a ladybird's route around this ring.

2 Make up your own mixed rings. Answer some questions about them.

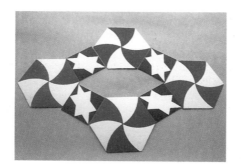 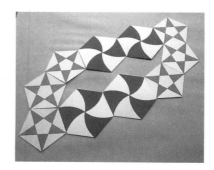

HOW BIG?

 For this activity use the fact that the side length of each ATM MAT is 6 cm.

1 Here is a ring made from 12 square ATM MATS.

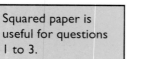
Squared paper is useful for questions 1 to 3.

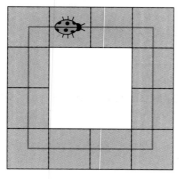

(a) A ladybird crawls around the ring as before. She goes from the centre of one MAT to the centre of the next.

How far does she crawl if she goes once around the ring? Give your answer in centimetres.

(b) Find the area of the hole in the ring in square centimetres.

(c) Find the total area of the MATS in square centimetres.

2 (a) Make some more rings from square MATS. Each ring should have a square hole in the middle.

(b) Find the distance the ladybird crawls around each of your rings.

(c) Find the area of the hole in each of your rings.

(d) Find the total area of the MATS in each ring.

(e) Look for patterns in your results.

3 (a) Make some rings from square MATS where the hole in the middle is *not* a square.

(b) Find the length of the ladybird's walk, the area of the hole and the area of the MATS for each of your rings.

4 Describe a ring made from square MATS where the length of the ladybird's crawl is as close as possible to 1 metre.

5 Describe a ring made from square MATS where the area of the hole is as close as possible to 1 square metre.

6 (a) Find the area of an ATM triangle MAT in square centimetres.

(b) Find the distance from the centre of the MAT to one of the sides in centimetres.

7 (a) Make some rings from triangle and hexagon MATS.

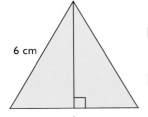

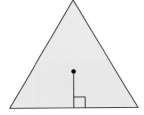

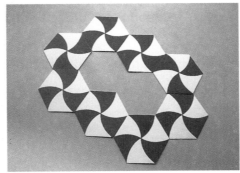 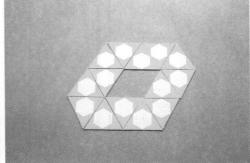

(b) Find the length of the ladybird's crawl for each of your rings.

(c) Find the area of the hole in each of your rings.

8 Describe a ring made of triangles and/or hexagons, where the length of the ladybird's crawl is almost exactly one metre.

9 Describe a ring made from triangles and/or hexagons, where the area of the hole is almost exactly one square metre.

Isometric dot paper is useful for questions 7 to 9.

A2
page
33

B9
page
60

RINGS OF SQUARE GENERATOR TILES

You will need squared paper for this activity. ATM generator tiles would also be useful.

 Here is a square ATM generator tile.

It can be used to make a pattern of rings like this.

Four tiles need to be used to form the inner ring.

1 Look at the pattern in the box above.

(a) How many tiles need to be added to form the second ring?

(b) How many tiles need to be added to form the third ring? The fourth ring? ...

(c) How many tiles need to be added to form the 20th ring?

(d) How many tiles need to be added to form the Nth ring?

(e) What is the *total* number of tiles needed for a pattern with 3 rings? 6 rings? 20 rings?

For question 2, you might find it helpful to draw a tile on squared paper.

2 The square tile is coloured by dividing each of the sides exactly into three.

(a) What fraction of the tile is black?

(b) What percentage of the tile is black?

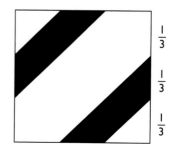

$\frac{1}{3}$

$\frac{1}{3}$

$\frac{1}{3}$

12

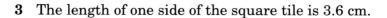

3 The length of one side of the square tile is 3.6 cm.

Find in square centimetres the area of the square tile which is black.

4 Look again at the picture in the box opposite.

(*a*) What is the area of black in the inner ring?

(*b*) What is the area of black in the second ring? The third ring? . . .

(*c*) A ladybird crawls around one of the rings in the *centre* of the black stripe. How far does she crawl?

 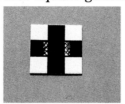 Other square generator tiles are coloured in a different way.

5 Make up your own ring patterns using square generator tiles. Use the tiles in whatever way you want.

Explore some of the properties of your ring patterns.

A2
page
33

F33
page
187

RINGS OF HEXAGON GENERATOR TILES

You will need the resource sheet *Hexagons* for this activity. ATM generator tiles would also be useful.

 Here is a hexagon generator tile.

Three of the tiles can be used to form a circular ring.

Here is a pattern formed from hexagon tiles.

1 (*a*) Look at the pattern in the box above. Three tiles are needed for the circle in the middle. How many tiles need to be added for the second ring?

(*b*) How many tiles need to be added for the third ring? Fourth ring? ...

(*c*) How many tiles need to be added for the 20th ring? The Nth ring?

(*d*) What is the total number of tiles needed for six rings? For 20 rings?

2 As for the square tile, the hexagon tile is coloured by dividing each of its sides exactly into three. The length of one side of the hexagon tile is 3.6 cm.

What percentage of the hexagon tile is coloured?

■ **3** Look at the pattern in the box opposite.

(a) A ladybird crawls around one of the rings in the *centre* of the black stripe. How far does she crawl?

(b) What is the area of black in the inner ring?

(c) What is the area of black in the second ring? The third ring? ...

(d) What is the area of white inside the inner ring? The second ring? ...

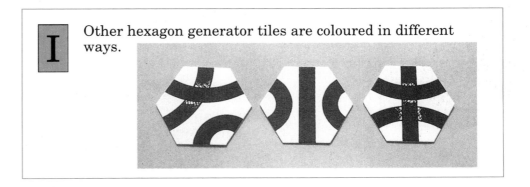

I Other hexagon generator tiles are coloured in different ways.

4 Make up your own ring patterns using hexagon generator tiles. Use whichever tiles you want.

Explore some of the properties of your ring patterns.

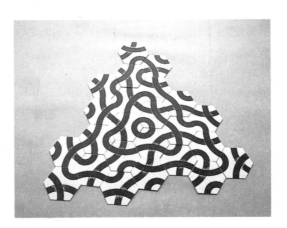

A2
page
33

F33
page
187

2 NOT LIKELY!

> What are the odds that I can get you to pick an ace from this pack of cards?

> It is very unlikely that the next person to walk through the door is wearing a diving suit.

> It is not very likely that I shall manage to throw a six first time.

EVENS CHANCE

1 Say whether each of the following is:

(A) an evens chance
(B) less than an evens chance
(C) more than an evens chance.

(*a*) You get a tail when you spin a coin.

(*b*) You get a six when you throw one dice.

(*c*) You get a red card when drawing one card from a pack of playing cards.

(*d*) A child born to a couple will be a girl.

(*e*) Two children born to a couple are the same sex.

(*f*) Three children born to a couple are all the same sex.

(*g*) You get one head and one tail when spinning two coins.

You might need to experiment to answer parts (h), (i) and (j).

(*h*) You get at least one spade when drawing two cards from a pack.

(*i*) You get no picture card when drawing three cards from a pack.

(*j*) You get at least one six when you throw three dice.

2 Make up some of your own problems like these. Give them to someone else to solve.

PICK A CARD

 You pick a card from a pack without looking.

There are 52 cards in a pack. 4 of them are aces.

So the probability that you pick an ace is $\frac{4}{52} = \frac{1}{13}$.

1 You pick a card from a pack.

(a) What is the probability that it is a black card?

(b) What is the probability that it is a spade?

(c) What is the probability that it is a picture card (a king, a queen or a jack)?

(d) What is the probability that it is not a picture card?

(e) What is the probability that it is the queen of hearts?

(f) What is the probability that it is a black king?

 Some cards have rotational symmetry and some do not.

For question 2 you will need to use a pack of cards.

2 (a) Which cards in a pack are symmetrical? How many are there?

(b) What is the probability of picking a symmetrical card from a pack?

3 A pack of cards is arranged into four piles, with all the clubs in one pile, all the hearts in another, all the spades in another, and all the diamonds in another.

You pick a card from one of the piles without looking.

(a) From which pile do you have the best chance of picking a symmetrical card?

(b) From which pile do you have the worst chance of picking a symmetrical card?

4 There is a card trick which uses all the non-symmetrical cards in a pack.

Make a pack of just the non-symmetrical cards. Shuffle it. Ask someone to pick a card without showing it to you. They then look at the card and put it back into the pack. You invite the person to shuffle the pack.

You then go through the pack and identify the card they picked. It's complete magic. How does it work?

TWO AT ONCE

 I Someone throws a dice and spins a coin.

There are 6 outcomes from throwing the dice.
There are 2 outcomes from spinning the coin.
So there are 12 outcomes altogether.

$$(1, H), (2, H), (3, H), (4, H), (5, H), (6, H),$$
$$(1, T), (2, T), (3, T), (4, T), (5, T), (6, T)$$

So the probability of getting any one of these, a 3 and a tail say, is $\frac{1}{12}$.

The probability of getting an odd number and a tail is $\frac{3}{12} = \frac{1}{4}$.

1 Someone throws a red dice and a blue dice.

(a) How many different outcomes are there?

(b) What is the probability of getting a 3 with the red dice and a 4 with the blue dice?

(c) What is the probability of getting a 5 on one dice and a 6 on the other?

(d) What is the probability of getting the same number on both dice?

(e) What is the probability that the sum of the two numbers thrown is 10?

2 Someone throws three dice.

(a) How many different outcomes are there?

(b) What is the probability of getting a 2 with all three dice?

(c) What is the probability of getting a 2, a 3 and a 5?

To do part (c) you need all the ways of getting 2, 3 and 5. Here are some:
(2, 3, 5),
(2, 5, 3),
(3, 2, 5), . . .

(d) What is the probability of getting the same number on all three dice?

(e) What is the probability of getting the same number on two of the dice?

(f) What is the probability that the sum of the three numbers thrown is 10?

 You pick two cards from a pack. What is the probability that the first is a heart and the second is a club?

There are 13 hearts in the pack so there are 13 ways out of 52 of getting a heart first.

There are 13 clubs in the pack so there are 13 ways out of 51 of getting a club second.

Altogether there are $13 \times 13 = 169$ ways out of $52 \times 51 = 2652$ of getting a heart and then a club.

So the probability is $\frac{169}{2652}$ or about 0.064.

Here is a slightly different problem. You pick two cards from a pack. What is the probability that one is a heart and one is a club?

This time it does not matter whether you pick heart followed by club, or club followed by heart.

The probability of each of these is $\frac{169}{2652}$.

So the probability of getting a heart and a club is $2 \times \frac{169}{2652}$ or about 0.127.

■ **3** Two cards are picked from a pack.

(*a*) What is the probability of getting a spade followed by a heart?

(*b*) What is the probability of getting a heart and a diamond?

 You pick two cards from a pack. What is the probability that they are both hearts?

There are 13 hearts in the pack so there are 13 ways out of 52 of getting a heart first.

There are now 12 hearts left in the pack so there are 12 ways out of 51 of getting a heart second.

Altogether there are $13 \times 12 = 156$ ways out of $52 \times 51 = 2652$ of getting a heart first and second.

So the probability is $\frac{156}{2652}$ or about 0.059.

■ **4** Two cards are picked from a pack.

(*a*) What is the probability of getting two red cards?

(*b*) What is the probability of getting two picture cards?

(*c*) What is the probability of not getting a picture card at all?

■ **5** Two people in your class are to be picked to do a job. All your names are put into a hat. Two are picked.

Write down your name and the name of someone else in the class. What is the probability that the two names you have written down will be picked?

A3
page
33

E25
page
152

COINCIDENCES

We are very impressed by some coincidences.

For example, you meet someone on holiday and you find you both know someone else.

Other coincidences do not impress us. Someone might forecast you are now being taught mathematics by a woman.

Sometimes coincidences impress us because they are very unlikely.

Sometimes they impress us because we *think* they are very unlikely.

1 Work with another person. Both think of a number less than 10.

Did you think of the same number? Is it a coincidence if you did?

What is the probability that you both think of the same number?

2 Suppose everybody in your class thinks of a number less than 10.

Is it a coincidence if everybody thinks of the same number? Would you be surprised?

Would you be surprised if two of the people thought of the same number?

3 A member of the Royal family is visiting your town. Someone in your class is to be picked to meet them. All your names are put into a bag. One name is picked out at random.

(*a*) What is the probability that you will be chosen?

(*b*) What is the probability that *someone* will be chosen?

(*c*) What is the probability that the person chosen will be female?

The population of the UK is 57 million.

4 (*a*) Would it be a coincidence if someone in your class has the same house number as you?

(*b*) Would it be a coincidence if there are two people in your class with the same house number? Find out whether it is true.

5

The chance of being killed by lightning in a year is supposed to be only 1 in ten million.

But that can't be true. The newspaper said six people in this country had been killed by lightning this year!

Is this argument logical?

■ 6 Here are the birth signs.

Aries	Libra
Taurus	Scorpio
Gemini	Sagittarius
Cancer	Capricorn
Leo	Aquarius
Virgo	Pisces

There are four types of birth sign: air, earth, fire and water. There are three birth signs of each type.

Someone wants to find out if people tend to marry other people with the same type of birth sign. They ask 60 couples. 16 of them have the same type of birth sign.

Does this prove that people do tend to marry other people with the same type of birth sign?

■ 7 Choose three other people so that you are in a group of four.

Get everyone in your group of four to throw a dice.

Now answer these questions. You will need to think about them carefully.

Hint first calculate the probability that no-one throws the same number as you.

(*a*) What is the probability that someone else throws the same number as you?

(*b*) Is it more likely that *any* two people will throw the same number? What is the probability of this?

■ 8 (*a*) What is the probability that someone in your group of four has the same birth month as you?

(*b*) Is it more likely that any two people in your group of four have the same birth month as each other? How likely do you think that is?

A3
page
33

3 RECTANGLES AND CUBOIDS

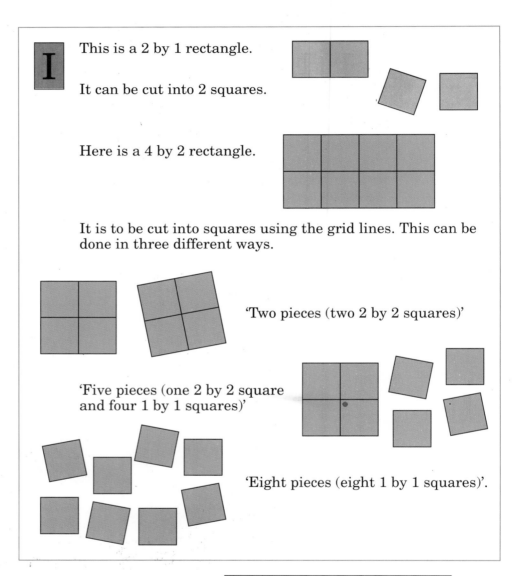

I This is a 2 by 1 rectangle.

It can be cut into 2 squares.

Here is a 4 by 2 rectangle.

It is to be cut into squares using the grid lines. This can be done in three different ways.

'Two pieces (two 2 by 2 squares)'

'Five pieces (one 2 by 2 square and four 1 by 1 squares)'

'Eight pieces (eight 1 by 1 squares)'.

1 Here is a 6 by 3 rectangle.

It is to be cut into squares using the grid lines.

In how many different ways can this be done? What is the total number of squares produced by each way?

2 (*a*) A 3 by 1 rectangle is cut into squares using the grid lines. In how many ways can this be done? How many squares do you get with each way?

(*b*) A 6 by 2 rectangle is cut into squares using the grid lines. In how many ways can this be done? How many squares do you get with each way?

(*c*) How many ways are there for a 9 by 3 rectangle? How many squares do you get with each way?

3 (*a*) How many ways are there for a 3 by 2 rectangle?

(*b*) How many ways are there for a 6 by 4 rectangle?

(*c*) How many ways are there for a 9 by 6 rectangle?

4 (*a*) What is the smallest number of squares a 5 by 3 rectangle can be cut into?

(*b*) Can it be cut into 7 squares? 8 squares? 9 squares?

(*c*) Into what other numbers of squares can a 5 by 3 rectangle be cut?

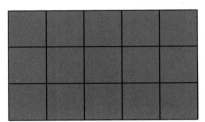

5 (*a*) What is the smallest number of squares a 7 by 6 rectangle can be cut into?

(*b*) Can it be cut into 7 squares? 8 squares? 9 squares?

(*c*) Into what other numbers of squares can a 7 by 6 rectangle be cut?

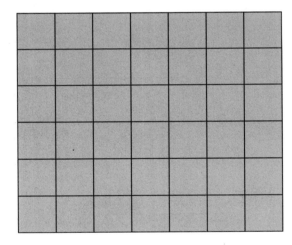

6 A 2 by 1 rectangle is to be cut into squares.

There are no grid lines. The rectangle can be cut anywhere.

It can obviously be cut into two squares. Into what other numbers of squares can it be cut?

Answer the same question for other rectangles.

You might want to discuss question 6 with other people.

CUTTING SQUARES OFF A RECTANGLE

You might have met this idea in Book 2.

 One method of cutting a rectangle into squares is to keep cutting off the biggest possible square.

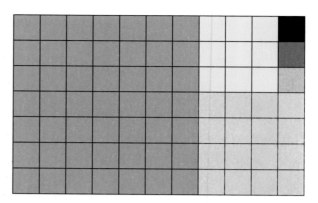

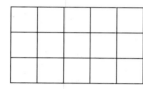

1 Draw a 5 by 3 rectangle.

Keep cutting the biggest possible square from it.

Into how many squares is the rectangle cut?

2 Answer question 1 for a 14 by 4 rectangle.

3 Answer question 1 for some other rectangles.

4 (a) If the method in the box above is used on an 8 by 3 rectangle:

    (i) how many squares are produced?
    (ii) how many different sizes of squares are produced?

  (b) Answer part (a) for an 8 by 4 rectangle. An 8 by 5 rectangle. An 8 by 6 rectangle. An 8 by 7 rectangle.

Which rectangle produces the largest number of different sized squares?

5 The longer side of a rectangle is 9. What should the shorter side be to produce the largest number of different sized squares?

What if the longer side was 10? Or 11? Or 12? Or . . .

6 Suppose you want to cut a rectangle into squares and to have as few squares as possible.

Sometimes the method in the box above produces the smallest possible number of squares. Sometimes it does not.

  (a) Find some rectangles where the method does produce the smallest possible number of squares.

  (b) Find some rectangles where the method does not produce the smallest possible number of squares.

A4
page
34

I The shape of a rectangle was first discussed on page 152 of Book 2.

One way to measure the shape of a rectangle is to divide the longer side by the shorter side. If this **sides' ratio** is the same for two rectangles then they are **similar** (the same shape).

For a 6 by 4 rectangle the **sides' ratio** is $\frac{6}{4} = 1.5$

For a 9 by 6 rectangle the **sides' ratio** is $\frac{9}{6} = 1.5$

So a 6 by 4 rectangle is **similar** to a 9 by 6 rectangle.

[the]re is another geometrical way to find out if two rectangles [are s]imilar. Place one of them on top of the other. If the [diago]nals of the rectangles coincide they are similar.

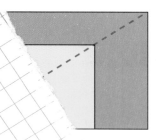
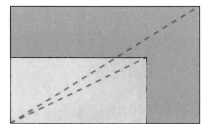

Not similar

1 Take a sheet [...] 'd it in half.

The new rectang[le...]

Compare the A5 rec[...] with another A4 rectangle.

Is the A5 rectangle similar to the A4 rectangle?

I An A4 rectangle can be obtained by halving an A3 rectangle.

An A3 rectangle can be obtained in the same way from an A2 rectangle.

And an A2 rectangle from an A1 rectangle.

And an A1 rectangle from an A0 rectangle.

■ 2 What fraction of the area of an A0 rectangle is an A4 rectangle?

■ 3 Take an A4 rectangle. Cut the largest possible square from it. Take the rectangle you are left with. Cut the largest possible square from that.

Compare the rectangle that remains with another A4 rectangle. What do you notice?

What will happen if you keep cutting squares from an A4 rectangle?

Let this side be x

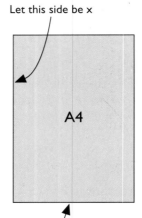

A4

Think of the length of the shorter side as 1

4 This question is about calculating the sides' ratio for an A4 sheet of paper.

    (*a*) What is the sides' ratio for this A4 rectangle?

The rectangle is folded in half to produce an A5 rectangle.

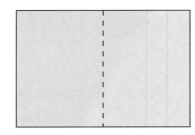

A5

    (*b*) How long are the sides of this A5 rectangle?

        What is the sides' ratio?

    (*c*) The A4 and the A5 rectangles are similar. So their sides' ratios must be the same. Use this fact to find *x*.

    (*d*) What is the sides' ratio for an A4 sheet of paper?

5 (*a*) What is the sides' ratio for a sheet of A0 paper?

    (*b*) The area of a sheet of A0 paper is 1 m². Use this fact to calculate the dimensions of a sheet of A0 paper.

    (*c*) Using your answer to question 4, calculate the dimensions of a sheet of A4 paper. Check your answer by measuring an A4 sheet.

6 (*a*) A square is cut from a sheet of A4 paper.

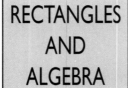

Using your answer to question 4, calculate the sides' ratio for the rectangle which is left.

A4 page 34

    (*b*) A square is cut from this rectangle. Calculate the sides' ratio for the rectangle which is left.

C17 page 91

Compare your result with your answer to question 3.

RECTANGLES AND ALGEBRA

1 Here is a rectangle divided into two rectangles.

    (*a*) Find the area of the large rectangle.

    (*b*) Find the areas of the two smaller rectangles.

    (*c*) What is the connection between the answers to parts (*a*) and (*b*)?

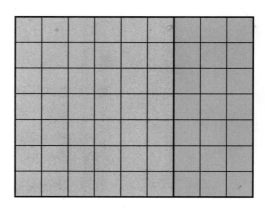

2 Here are two rectangles. Each rectangle has been cut into two pieces.

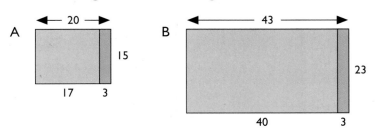

A — 20 — 15 — 17 — 3

B — 43 — 23 — 40 — 3

(a) Find the total area of each of the big rectangles without using a calculator.

(b) How did you do this for rectangle A?

(c) How did you do this for rectangle B?

3 Make up some more rectangles divided into two pieces.

Find their areas without using a calculator.

Give them to someone else to find their areas.

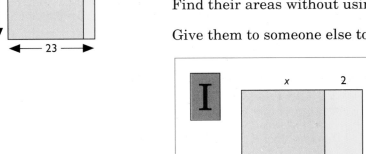

20   3
7
37   30
23

4 Here is a rectangle divided into 4 pieces.

Find its area without using a calculator.

5 Make up some more rectangles divided into four pieces.

Find their areas without using a calculator.

Give them to someone else to find their areas.

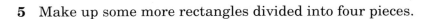

I

x   2
3
x + 2

Here is a rectangle divided into two pieces.

The area of the large rectangle is $3(x + 2)$. The areas of the two smaller rectangles are $3x$ and 6.

So $3(x + 2) = 3x + 6$

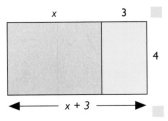

x   3
4
x + 3

6 Here is a rectangle divided into two pieces.

(a) Find the area of the large rectangle.

(b) Find the areas of the two smaller rectangles.

(c) What is the connection between the answers to parts (a) and (b)?

7 Answer question 6 for each of these rectangles.

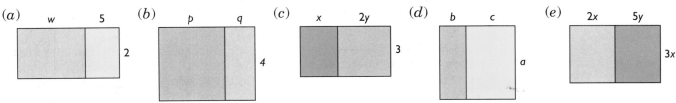

(a) w   5   2

(b) p   q   4

(c) x   2y   3

(d) b   c   a

(e) 2x   5y   3x

■ **8** Here are some algebraic expressions. Some of them are the areas of larger rectangles. Some of them are areas of two small rectangles added together.

Write each of them in a different way.

(a) $3x + 9$ (b) $4(z + 4)$ (c) $4a + 4b$ (d) $3(c + 2d)$

(e) $ap + aq$ (f) $bt + 2ct$ (g) $x(x + y)$ (h) $a^2x + ax^2$

■ **9** Make up some more examples like those in question 8. Give them to someone else to solve.

■ **10** (a) What is another way of writing $3(a + b + 5)$?

(b) Draw a picture for part (a)

■ **11** Write these in another way.

(a) $5(p + q + 4)$ (b) $a(b + c + d)$ (c) $x(x + y + z)$

(d) $3c + 3d + 3e$ (e) $4x + 4y + 12z$

■ **12** Make up some more examples like those in question 11. Give them to someone else to solve.

■ **13** (a) What is another way of writing $5(g - 3)$?

(b) Draw a picture for part (a).

■ **14** Make up some more examples like the one in question 13.

 Here is a rectangle divided into four pieces.

The area of the large rectangle is $(x + 1)(y + 2)$. The areas of the four smaller rectangles are xy, $2x$, y and 2.

So $(x + 1)(y + 2) = xy + 2x + y + 2$

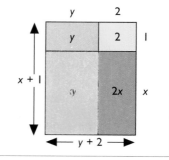

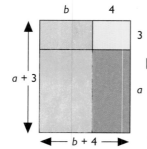

■ **15** Here is a rectangle divided into four pieces.

(a) Find the area of the large rectangle.

(b) Find the areas of the smaller rectangles.

(c) What is the connection between the answers to parts (a) and (b)?

■ **16** Find another way of writing these.

(a) $(p + 1)(q + 2)$ (b) $(x + 3)(z + 4)$ (c) $(a + b)(c + d)$

(d) $(x + 3)(x + 4)$ (e) $(u + v)(u + w)$

A4 page 34   A5 page 35

■ **17** Make up some more examples like those in question 16. Give them to someone else to solve. (You could give them the question. Or you could give them the answer and they could try to find the question.)

BREAKING A CUBOID INTO CUBES

You might find interlocking cubes useful for this activity. You might also find isometric dot paper useful.

 This is a 2 by 2 by 1 cuboid made of interlocking cubes.

It can be broken into 4 cubes.

This is a 4 by 4 by 2 cuboid made of interlocking cubes.

It can be broken into cubes in five different ways.

4 cubes

11 cubes

18 cubes

25 cubes

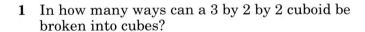
32 cubes

1 In how many ways can a 3 by 2 by 2 cuboid be broken into cubes?

How many cubes do you get with each way?

2 In how many ways can a 6 by 4 by 2 cuboid be broken into cubes?

How many cubes do you get with each way?

3 What is the smallest number of cubes into which a 5 by 4 by 3 cuboid can be broken?

4 Investigate the numbers of cubes into which other cuboids can be broken.

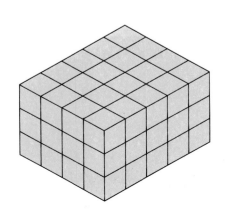

 F34 page 188

 F35 page 189

CUTTING A CUBOID INTO SQUARE PRISMS

You might find interlocking cubes useful for this activity. You might also find isometric dot paper useful.

 A square prism is a cuboid with at least two square faces. In other words, at least two of its dimensions are equal.

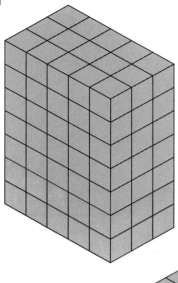

If you start with a 5 by 3 by 7 cuboid and cut off the *biggest* possible square prism, you are left with a 5 by 3 by 2 cuboid.

If the biggest possible square prism is again cut off a 5 by 1 by 2 cuboid is left. If the process is repeated again

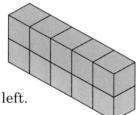

a 5 by 1 by 1 square prism is left.

Once you have a square prism left you stop.

1 What square prism do you end up with if you cut square prisms from a 5 by 3 by 2 cuboid?

2 What square prism do you end up with if you cut square prisms from an 8 by 6 by 4 cuboid?

3 Try cutting square prisms from other cuboids.

Try to predict what will happen in *some* cases. (It is difficult to find a general rule that works for *all* cases.)

F34
page
188

F35
page
189

3-D COORDINATES

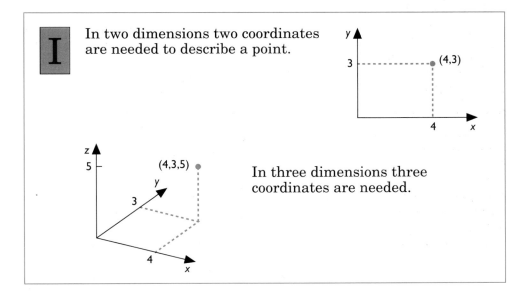

I In two dimensions two coordinates are needed to describe a point.

In three dimensions three coordinates are needed.

■ **1** A cube with sides of length 3 has its sides parallel to the coordinate axes. One corner is at the origin.

(*a*) What are the coordinates of the other seven corners, assuming that none of these coordinates is negative?

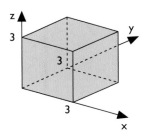

(*b*) If some of the coordinates can be negative, how many positions are there for the corner of the cube diagonally opposite the corner at the origin? What are the coordinates of these positions?

■ **2** Two adjacent corners of a cube are at (4, 3, 5) and (4, 8, 5). The edges of the cubes are parallel to the coordinate axes.

Give the coordinates of the other corners of the cube. There is more than one possible answer.

■ **3** A cuboid has dimensions 2 by 2 by 3. The edges of the cuboid are parallel to the coordinate axes.

One corner of the cuboid is at (1, 1, 1). Give the coordinates of all possible positions for the diagonally opposite corner.

■ **4** A cube has one corner at the origin and an adjacent corner at (0, 3, 4). The coordinates of the corner diagonally opposite the corner at the origin are all positive.

Find the coordinates of the corners of the cube.

Find the coordinates of the centre of each face.

A6
page
35

REVIEW EXERCISES A

Angles and Symmetry

1 Find the missing angle in each of these shapes:

(*a*)

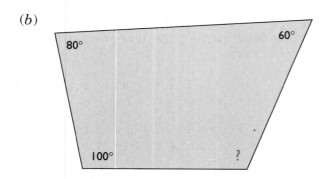

(*b*)

2 (*a*) What are the angles of a right-angled isosceles triangle?

(*b*) What are the angles of an equilateral triangle?

(*c*) What are the angles of a regular hexagon?

3 (*a*) One of the angles of a parallelogram is 50°. What are the other three angles?

(*b*) Describe the symmetry of this parallelogram.

4 (*a*) Two of the angles of a kite are 140° and 120°. What are the other two angles?

(*b*) Describe the symmetry of this kite.

5 What are the four angles labelled A, B, C and D?

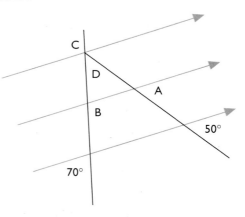

6 (*a*) Describe the symmetry of each of these dominoes.

Altogether there are 28 dominoes in this set.

(*b*) Which of these 28 dominoes have line symmetry?

(*c*) Which of the 28 dominoes have rotational symmetry?

7 In the hexagon ABCDEF, AF is parallel to BC and EF is parallel to DC.

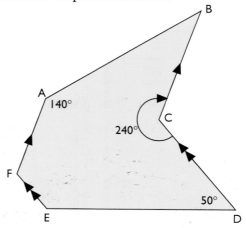

Three of the angles are shown. Find the other three angles of the hexagon.

EXERCISE 2 Perimeter and Area

1 Find the perimeter and area of each of these shapes.

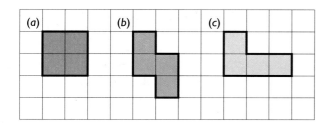

2 (a) Draw on squared paper three rectangles with an area of 24 cm².

(b) Find the perimeter of each of the rectangles you drew for (a).

3 Find the areas of these triangles.

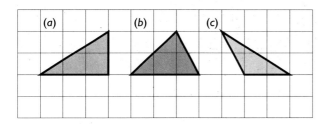

4 (a) Draw accurately three different triangles with a perimeter of 18 cm.

(b) By measuring the triangles you drew for (a) estimate their areas.

5 (a) The diameter of a circle is 1 metre. What is its circumference?

(b) The radius of a circle is 1 metre. What is its circumference?

(c) The circumference of a circle is 1 metre. What is its radius?

6 (a) The diameter of a circle is 30 cm. What is its area?

(b) The area of a circle is 30 cm². What is its radius?

7 This picture shows how an athletics field is marked out for the shot put.

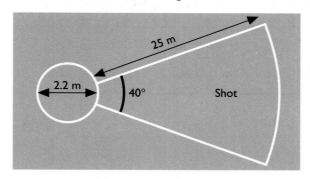

(a) What is the total length of the lines used?

(b) What is the total area inside the lines?

EXERCISE 3 Probability I

1 Is each of the following (A) an evens chance (B) better than evens chance (C) worse than an evens chance?

(a) The chance of getting a head when you spin a coin.

(b) The chance that the next person you meet has the same birth month as you.

(c) The chance of getting an even number when you throw a dice.

(d) The chance of getting two heads when you spin two coins.

(e) The chance that the next bus driver you see is male.

2 What is the probability of each of the following?

(a) Getting a tail when you spin a coin.

(b) Getting a 6 when you throw a dice.

(c) Getting a spade when you cut a pack of cards.

(d) Getting an ace when you cut a pack of cards.

(e) The next person you meet was born in a month with an *r* in it.

(f) The next person you meet was born on a day of the week with a *u* in it.

3 Two dice are thrown. The numbers they show are added to give a score.

Copy and complete this table of possible outcomes.

Score on second dice

	1	2	3	4	5	6
1						
2		4			7	
3						
4						10
5	6					
6				10		

Score on first dice

(a) What is the probability that the score will be even?

(b) What is the probability that the score will be a multiple of 3?

(c) What is the probability that the score will be a multiple of 4?

(d) What is the probability that the score will be a multiple of 5?

(e) What is the probability that the score will be a multiple of 6?

(f) What is the probability that the score will be a multiple of 7?

EXERCISE 4 Properties of Numbers

1 Write these numbers in order of size, starting with the smallest.

9000, 900, 9999, 90, 9090, 999, 9990, 9900, 990, 9009, 909, 99, 9909

2 (a) What are the factors of 18?

(b) Which of the factors of 18 are also factors of 30?

3 Do not use your calculator for this question. The diagram below shows a rectangle 57 units by 24 units.

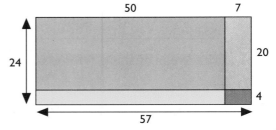

Find the area of each of the four pieces of the rectangle.

What is 57×24?

4 Here are three sequences

A: 1, 3, 5, 7, 9, 11 ...

B: 12, 17, 22, 27, ...

C: 13, 16, 19, 22, ...

D: 10, 17, 24, 31, 38 ...

(a) Write down the next two terms of each sequence.

(b) Which of the sequences includes the number 57?

(c) Which of the sequences includes the number 100?

(d) Which of the sequences includes the number 710?

(e) Which of the sequences includes the number 1009?

6 Arrange these numbers in order of size:

3.16, $\frac{223}{71}$, $\sqrt{10}$, π, 3.142, $\frac{22}{7}$, $\sqrt[3]{31}$, 1.78^2, $\frac{355}{113}$

EXERCISE 5 Using Brackets

1 Write the following without brackets:

(a) $2(x + 3)$ (b) $3(a + 5)$

(c) $4(d - 4)$ (d) $6(f - 9)$

2 Write the following without brackets:

(a) $a(b + c)$ (b) $x(y + 4)$ (c) $p(q - r)$

(d) $e(f + 2g)$ (e) $2x(y - 3z)$

3 Write the following without brackets:

(a) $a(a + b)$ (b) $x(x - y)$

(c) $t(2s + 3t)$ (d) $2p(2p - 3q)$

4 Write the following using brackets:

(a) $5a + 5b$ (b) $6x - 6y$ (c) $2c + 4d$

(d) $rs + rt$ (e) $3u - 9$ (f) $xy + 2xz$

5 Write the following using brackets:

(a) $2ab + 6ac$ (b) $p^2 + 4pq$ (c) $3x^2 - 9xy$

(d) $ab + ac + ad$ (e) $4r^2 + 6rs + 8rt$

6 Gurpaul and Emily were both solving a problem about the areas of triangles drawn on an isometric grid. Gurpaul said that the formula for the area was $(m - n)^2 + 3mn$. Emily said the formula for the area was $m^2 + n^2 + mn$.

Do their answers agree?

7 Jane and Bob were both solving a problem about the areas of equiangular hexagons. Jane said that the formula for the area was $(m + n + p)^2 - m^2 - n^2 - p^2$. Bob said the formula for the area was $mn + np + mp$.

Do their answers agree?

EXERCISE 6 3-D Coordinates

1 Find the distance of each of these points from the origin.

(a) $(3, 0, 0)$ (b) $(0, -5, 0)$ (c) $(3, 4, 0)$

(d) $(0, 5, -12)$ (e) $(4, 4, -2)$

2 A is at $(4, 2, -1)$, B is at $(4, 2, 2)$ and C is at $(2, 0, 0)$.

What sort of triangle is ABC?

3 A cuboid has one corner at the origin and the opposite corner at the point $(4, 8, 6)$. The table the cuboid is resting on is the xy-plane.

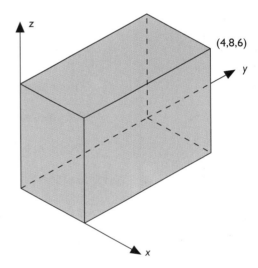

There are four directions in which the cuboid could be toppled. Find the coordinates of the farthest corner of the cuboid from the origin after each of these four topples.

4 The point P is at $(4, -3, 2)$. What are the coordinates of the point obtained by

(a) reflecting P in the xy-plane?

(b) reflecting P in the xz-plane?

(c) rotating P through 180° about the x-axis?

(d) rotating P through 90° anticlockwise about the positive y-axis?

4 THE ANSWER IS 4t + 2

THE ANSWER IS 2x + 6

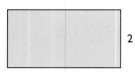

x + 3

2

1 (a) What is the perimeter of this triangle?

(b) Draw a sketch of another triangle which has a perimeter of 2x + 6.

2 Draw sketches of some quadrilaterals with a perimeter of 2x + 6.

3 What is the area of this rectangle?

4 Draw some other shapes which have an area of 2x + 6.

x   x

6

THE ANSWER IS 6x + 12

1 Draw some shapes which have a perimeter of 6x + 12.

2 Draw some shapes which have an area of 6x + 12.

3 There are 6 bags. In each bag there is the same number of cubes.

Two more cubes are added to each bag.

There are 6x + 12 cubes in the bags altogether. What is x?

4 Matches are used to make a hexagon in the middle of a row of squares.

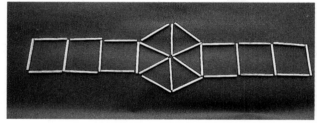

If the number of matches is 6x + 12, what is x?

5 I think of a number and double it. Then I add on 4. Then I multiply by 3. What is the answer?

6 Make up some more problems which have the answer 6x + 12.

B7 page 58

THE ANSWER IS . . .

1 This question is about $x^2 + 2x + 1$.

(a) What is the value of $x^2 + 2x + 1$

(i) if $x = 1$?   (ii) if $x = 2$?   (iii) if $x = 4$?

(b) Choose some other positive whole numbers for x and find the value of $x^2 + 2x + 1$ for each of them.

You might find *Spread* useful for this activity.

(c) Choose some negative whole numbers for x and find the value of $x^2 + 2x + 1$ for each of them.

(d) What do all the answers to parts (a), (b) and (c) have in common? Will this always be true?

(e) What is the smallest value you can get for $x^2 + 2x + 1$?

2 This question is about $x^2 - x$.

(a) What is the value of $x^2 - x$

(i) if $x = 2$?   (ii) if $x = 3$?   (iii) if $x = 5$?

(b) Choose some other positive whole numbers for x and find the value of $x^2 - x$ for each of them.

(c) Choose some negative whole numbers for x and find the value of $x^2 - x$ for each of them.

(d) What do all the answers to parts (a), (b) and (c) have in common? Will this always be true?

(e) What is the smallest value you can get for $x^2 - x$ if x is a whole number?

(f) What is the smallest value you can get for $x^2 - x$ if x does not have to be a whole number?

3 Make up some formulae where the value is always odd if x is a whole number.

4 This question is about $x^3 - x + 9$.

(a) Choose some positive and negative whole numbers for x and find the value of $x^3 - x + 9$ for each of them.

(b) What do all your answers to part (a) have in common? Will this always be true?

(c) Find the three values of x which make $x^3 - x + 9$ equal to 9. What happens to $x^3 - x + 9$ between these values?

5 Make up some formulae where the value is always a multiple of 4 if x is a whole number.

6 Make up some formulae where the value is always a multiple of 6 if x is a whole number.

7 This question is about the formulae $x^2 + x + 5$ and $x^2 - x + 5$.

(a) Choose some positive whole numbers for x and find the value of $x^2 - x + 5$.

(b) Choose some negative whole numbers for x and find the value of $x^2 + x + 5$.

(c) What do you notice about your answers to (a) and (b)?

8 Find some other pairs of formulae which give the same answers.

B8 page 59

THE ANSWER IS $2x^2 + 4x$

■ **1** The area of this rectangle is $2x^2 + 4x$.

Suggest suitable lengths for its sides.

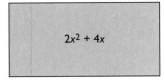

■ **2** The area of this triangle is $2x^2 + 4x$.

Suggest suitable dimensions for the triangle.

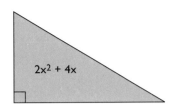

■ **3** The perimeter of a rectangle is $2x^2 + 4x$.

Suggest suitable dimensions for the rectangle.

■ **4** I think of a number and add 1. I square the answer. I then multiply by 2 and subtract 2.

What is the answer?

■ **5** Make up some more problems to which the answer is $2x^2 + 4x$.

YOU CHOOSE

1 Choose your own formula. Make up some problems which have your formula as the answer.

B7
page
58

ODD AND EVEN NUMBERS

 1 (a) What happens when you divide an even number by 2?

(b) What happens when you divide an odd number by 2?

> **I** The answer to part (b) of question 1 gives us a way of making up an algebraic formula which will give all the odd numbers.
>
> The formula $2N + 1$ gives an odd number provided N is a whole number.
>
> If you think of *any* odd number you will be able to find a value for N so that $2N + 1$ gives the number you are thinking of.

2 What odd numbers do the following values of *N* give?

    (*a*) *N* = 2   (*b*) *N* = 5   (*c*) *N* = 53

3 What values of *N* give the following odd numbers?

    (*a*) 7   (*b*) 21   (*c*) 99

4 Try some negative whole number values for *N*. Do you still get odd numbers?

5 Write down a formula which will give all the even numbers.

How does your formula give these even numbers?

    (*a*) 6   (*b*) 124   (*c*) 1000

6 Does your even number formula work for negative numbers?

7 What happens if you double an odd number and then divide the result by 4?

Explain why this happens by using the odd number formula.

8 What happens if you square an odd number and then divide the result by 4? Explain this by using the odd number formula.

9 What happens if you square an even number and then divide the result by 4?

Explain this by using your even number formula.

A different formula for odd numbers is *2M* + *1*. Yet another formula is *2P* + *1*, *2x* + *1* or *2a* + *1*.

It doesn't matter what letter you use: if the value of the letter is a whole number the formula will give an odd number.

Suppose you want to write down formulae for two *different* odd numbers (you don't know what the odd numbers are). It would be confusing to say the odd numbers are

2N + *1* and *2N* + *1*

because then it looks as if the odd numbers are the *same*.

So you could say the odd numbers are

2M + *1* and *2N* + *1*

---

10 Use the idea in the box above to explain why the sum of two odd numbers is an even number.

11 Use the idea in the box above to explain why the product of two odd numbers is an odd number.

Here is a way of dividing all the positive whole numbers into three sets:

> A: 1, 4, 7, 10, 13, 16, 19, 22, . . .
> B: 2, 5, 8, 11, 14, 17, 20, 23, . . .
> C: 3, 6, 9, 12, 15, 18, 21, 24, . . .

■ **12** (*a*) Write down a formula which gives all the numbers in row A in the box above.

(*b*) Write down a formula which gives all the numbers in row B.

(*c*) Write down a formula which gives all the numbers in row C.

■ **13** Choose a number in row B and double it. Which row is the answer in? Is the answer always in the same row?

Explain your result using one of your formulae.

■ **14** Choose a number in row A and double it. Which row is the answer in? Is the answer always in the same row?

Explain your result using one of your formulae.

■ **15** Choose a number in row B and square it. Which row is the answer in? Is the answer always in the same row?

Explain your result using one of your formulae.

■ **16** Choose a number in row A and square it. Which row is the answer in? Is the answer always in the same row?

Explain your results using one of your formulae.

B8 page 59

PYTHAGOREAN TRIANGLE FORMULAE

 Pythagorean triangles were first introduced in Book 2.

A **Pythagorean triangle** is a right-angled triangle. The lengths of its sides must all be whole numbers.

Here are two Pythagorean triangles:

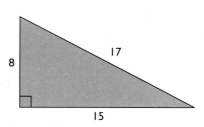

1 Two examples of Pythagorean triangles are given in the box above. Give two more examples of Pythagorean triangles.

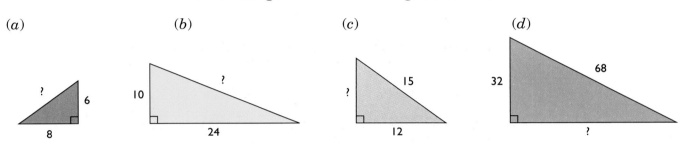

I If you know one Pythagorean triangle you can use it to find as many others as you like. You simply make them similar (the same shape but a different size). For example, if you know that this is a Pythagorean triangle

then so are these.

2 Here are some Pythagorean triangles with missing sides. Try to fill in the missing side without having to calculate it.

(*a*)   (*b*)   (*c*)   (*d*)

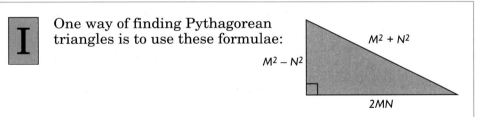

I One way of finding Pythagorean triangles is to use these formulae:

$$M^2 - N^2$$
$$M^2 + N^2$$
$$2MN$$

If you substitute whole numbers for *M* and *N* these formulae give the three sides of a Pythagorean triangle.

In fact, *all* Pythagorean triangles can be found using these formulae.

You might find *Spread* useful for questions 3, 4 and 5.

3 Use the formulae in the box above to find some Pythagorean triangles.

4 What are the values of *M* and *N* which produce these triangles:

(*a*) 3, 4, 5?   (*b*) 5, 12, 13?   (*c*) 20, 21, 29?

5 What values of *M* and *N* give a Pythagorean triangle, one of whose sides is 42?

6 Because the three Pythagorean triangle formulae give the sides of a right-angled triangle, they must obey Pythagoras' theorem.

Prove that they do. (Use algebra. Do not substitute numbers.)

B8 page 59

C17 page 91   B9 page 60

DESIGN A CHAIR

To be comfortable a chair needs to be the right size for the person sitting on it.

How do the people who make chairs decide what size to make them?

YOUR CLASSROOM CHAIRS

1 Use a tape measure to find the height, width, depth . . . of a chair in your classroom. Furniture is usually measured in millimetres.

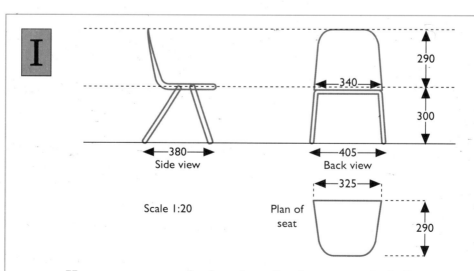

I

290

340

300

←380→
Side view

←405→
Back view

Scale 1:20

Plan of seat

←325→

290

Here are some scale drawing of a classroom chair from a classroom for five-year-olds. Measurements are to the nearest 5 mm.

C13 page 88

2 Make accurate scale drawings for the chair you have measured.

3 Look at the differences between your chair and the chair designed for five-year-olds. The manufacturers have made them different because five-year-olds are smaller than fourteen-year-olds.

Make a list of the body measurements it is important to know if you are designing a chair.

HOW BIG SHOULD A CHAIR BE?

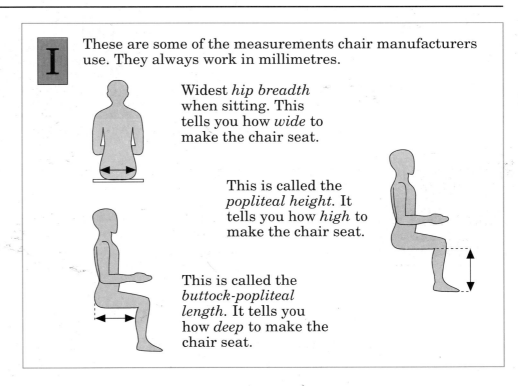

I These are some of the measurements chair manufacturers use. They always work in millimetres.

Widest *hip breadth* when sitting. This tells you how *wide* to make the chair seat.

This is called the *popliteal height*. It tells you how *high* to make the chair seat.

This is called the *buttock-popliteal length*. It tells you how *deep* to make the chair seat.

If you do not want to collect measurements for your class use the resource sheet *Anthropometric data for a class of 14-year-olds*.

1 Find out the three measurements described in the box above for everyone in your class. People must be sitting down, as shown in the pictures, to get the correct measurements.

Make sure you know which measurements are for boys and which are for girls.

I Suppose you decided that you could only measure accurately to the nearest 10 mm. Then a recorded hip breadth of 370 mm means that the hip breadth is between 365 mm and 375 mm.

2 (a) What order of accuracy did you use for your measurements?

(b) Choose several of your measurements. Write down the limits between which the measured lengths must lie.

3 (a) Find the mean for your class for each of the three measurements. Give your answers to a sensible degree of accuracy.

(b) How well does your classroom chair fit with the mean measurements? Do you think that mean measurements would be helpful to chair designers?

B10 page 61

DO LONG-LEGGED PEOPLE HAVE BROAD HIPS?

You can either use the measurements for your class or the resource sheet *Anthropometric data for a class of 14-year-olds.*

I Look at this scatter graph. It shows the popliteal height and buttock-popliteal length for 20 fourteen-year-olds.

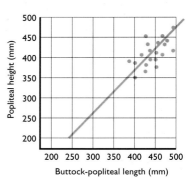

Not surprisingly, it looks as if people with bigger popliteal height tend to have a bigger buttock-popliteal measurement. This is described by saying that there is a **positive correlation** between these two measurements.

One way of showing the positive correlation is to draw a **line of best fit**. This is shown in red on the graph.

You can use the line of best fit to make predictions. For example, you might predict that someone with a popliteal height of 350 mm is likely to have a buttock-popliteal length of about 380 mm. A different person with a buttock-popliteal length of 450 mm is likely to have a popliteal height of about 420 mm.

1 (a) Draw a scatter graph, like the one in the box above for your set of measurements. You might want to mark the results for boys and for girls with different symbols.

(b) Draw the line of best fit.

(c) Use your line to make some predictions. How accurate do you think your predictions are?

2 (a) Draw a scatter graph to show hip breadth compared to buttock-popliteal length. You could draw separate graphs for boys and for girls.

(b) Does your diagram suggest that these measurements are correlated?

(c) Do long-legged people have broad hips?

B11
page
62

WORKING WITH LOTS OF DATA

I Chair manufacturers need to be sure that their chairs will be comfortable for lots of people. To do this they collect measurements from a large number of people. Here are the results one manufacturer collected from 100 adults, including both men and women. The results are grouped into class intervals of 20 mm to make it easier for the data to be analysed.

Measurement (mm)	Popliteal height (freq)	Buttock-popliteal length (freq)	Hip breadth (freq)
300 ≤ m < 320	0	0	10
320 ≤ m < 340	3	0	12
340 ≤ m < 360	8	0	13
360 ≤ m < 380	14	0	18
380 ≤ m < 400	15	2	21
400 ≤ m < 420	17	3	14
420 ≤ m < 440	14	9	8
440 ≤ m < 460	13	13	3
460 ≤ m < 480	7	18	1
480 ≤ m < 500	6	22	0
500 ≤ m < 520	2	19	0
520 ≤ m < 540	1	10	0
540 ≤ m < 560	0	3	0
560 ≤ m < 580	0	1	0

This means that 17 people have a popliteal height of between 400 mm and 420 mm.

This is how you work out the mean popliteal height for the 100 people.

This interval includes all measurements of 320 and more but less than 340.

Measurement (mm)	Popliteal height (freq)	Middle value (mm)	Frequency × middle value
320 ≤ m < 340	3	330	990
340 ≤ m < 360	8	350	2800
360 ≤ m < 380	14	370	5180
380 ≤ m < 400	15	390	5850
400 ≤ m < 420	17	410	6970
420 ≤ m < 440	14	430	6020
440 ≤ m < 460	13	450	5850
460 ≤ m < 480	7	470	3290
480 ≤ m < 500	6	490	2940
500 ≤ m < 520	2	510	1020
520 ≤ m < 540	1	530	530
	100		41440

mean = 41440 ÷ 100 = 414 mm

■ 1 Find the mean buttock-popliteal length for the 100 people.

■ 2 Find the mean hip breadth of the 100 people.

The technique you have just used assumes that the measurements collected are *exact*. This is not actually a sensible assumption.

More realistically, suppose the measurements collected were all measured to the nearest 10 mm. This means, for example, the interval 320 ≤ m < 340 includes only the measurements 320 and 330. So the middle value of this interval is *not* 330! It is in fact 325.

■ 3 Assuming that the measurements given are all measured to the nearest 10 mm, recalculate the mean for buttock-popliteal length and hip breadth.

Give your answers to a sensible degree of accuracy.

Are the answers significantly different from those obtained for questions 1 and 2?

■ 4 How well does your classroom chair fit the mean measurements for the 100 adults?

B11
page
62

DESIGN A CHAIR TO SUIT MOST PEOPLE

Manufacturers cannot make a chair which will suit everyone. They have to decide on a size which will be comfortable for most people. One way in which they could do this is to use mean measurements like those you calculated in the previous section. But if they simply used the mean measurements to design the chair a lot of people would find it too high or too deep. Instead, manufacturers work with **percentile** measurements. This activity is about how such measurements are worked out.

This diagram is called a **cumulative frequency curve**. It shows what percentages of five-year-old children have different popliteal heights.

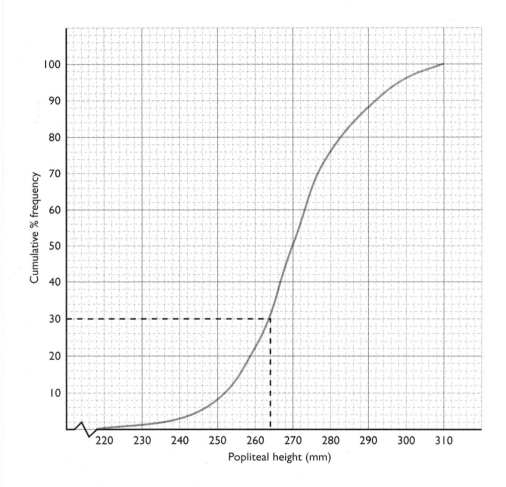

The diagram shows, for example, that 30% of five-year-old children have a popliteal height which is less than or equal to 265 mm (to the nearest 5 mm). This means that 70% of them have a popliteal height of more than 265 mm.

■ **1** Use the graph in the box opposite to complete these statements.

  (*a*) 60% of five-year-old children have a popliteal height of _____ or less.

  (*b*) _____ % of five-year-old children have a popliteal height of 250 mm or less.

  (*c*) 15% of five-year-old children have a popliteal height of more than _____ .

  (*d*) _____ % of five-year-old children have a popliteal height of more than 290 mm.

 The **median** popliteal height (or **50th percentile**) is the middle measurement. In other words, 50% of the children have a smaller popliteal height than the median and 50% have a larger popliteal height.

■ **2** Use the graph to find the median popliteal height for five-year-olds.

 The **lower quartile** is the **25th percentile.** One quarter (25%) of the population is less than the lower quartile and three quarters (75%) is more than it.

The **upper quartile** is the **75th percentile**. Three quarters (75%) of the population is less than the upper quartile and one quarter (25%) is more than it.

■ **3** Find the lower and upper quartile popliteal heights for five-year-olds.

 The **inter-quartile range** is the difference between the lower quartile and the upper quartile. It gives you an idea of how spread out the measurements are. A large inter-quartile range tells you that the measurements vary a lot from one person to another.

■ **4** Work out the inter-quartile range for popliteal height for five-year-olds.

 Chair manufacturers design chairs so that 95% of people using them will find them comfortable.

■ **5** (*a*) What height should a chair for five-year-olds be so that 95% of them can reach the floor easily when sitting on it properly?

  (*b*) The chair drawn at the start of the chapter has a seat which is 300 mm from the floor.

  What percentage of five-year-olds would be able to reach the floor when sitting properly on the chair?

  (*c*) Does your answer to part (b) surprise you? Can you think of an explanation?

B11 page 62

This cumulative frequency table shows the way in which buttock-popliteal lengths for five-year-olds are distributed.

Buttock-popliteal length less than (mm)	Percentage of 5-year-olds	Cumulative percentage
230	0	0
240	1	1
250	2	3
260	5	8
270	12	20
280	18	38
290	26	64
300	16	80
310	10	90
320	5	95
330	3	98
340	2	100

This means that 12% of five-year-olds have a buttock-popliteal length of less than 270 mm but more than 260 mm.

This means that 20% of five-year-olds have a buttock-popliteal length of less than 270 mm.

■ **6** (a) Draw a cumulative frequency curve for the data in the box above.

(b) Use your curve to make some statements similar to those in question 1.

(c) Find the median, lower quartile and upper quartile buttock-popliteal lengths.

(d) Find the inter-quartile range. Compare this with the inter-quartile range for popliteal height. What can you conclude?

(e) How deep should the seat of a chair be so that 95% of five-year-olds could sit back on it and still be able to bend their knees?

(f) The chair drawn at the start of the chapter has a seat depth of 290 mm. What percentage of 5-year-olds would be able to bend their knees when sitting on that chair?

DESIGN A CHAIR FOR YOUR CLASS

You can either use the measurements for your class or the resource sheet *Anthropometric data for a class of 14-year-olds.*

Use the ideas in the previous section to analyse the data you have collected for your class. How well does your classroom chair suit you all?

You might want to compare your class results with the British Standards measurements given in the table on the next page.

Anthropometric data for fourteen-year-olds

	Boys			Girls			Combined		
	5th	50th	95th	5th	50th	95th	5th	50th	95th
		percentiles			percentiles			percentiles	
Popliteal height (mm)	375	425	470	355	395	435	360	410	460
Buttock-popliteal length (mm)	405	460	515	415	455	500	410	460	505
Hip breadth (mm)	260	305	355	285	330	370	270	320	365

E28
page
154

- Draw a percentage cumulative frequency curve for each of the three measurements.
- Find the medians, quartiles and inter-quartile ranges.
- Find the 5th and 95th percentiles.
- What percentage of your class are likely to find the chair suitable?
- Would you recommend different measurements for a chair which was ideally suitable for your class?

DESIGN A...

Use the ideas presented in this task to design your own piece of furniture. Or to design a child's toy. Or . . .

The *anthropometric data* resource sheets will be helpful.

6 FIND THE NUMBER

GUESS THE NUMBER

I Here is a game for a group of players. It could be played by the whole class.

Someone thinks of a whole number between 1 and 15.

Everyone else has to guess what number has been thought of. Someone makes a first guess: 6 say. The person who thought of the number then says whether the guess is

> the right number
> or too high
> or too low.

The computer program *Spread* could be used for this game.

Set *Spread* up with one row and one column.

Enter the formula RND(15).

Press H to hide the number. Press U to update the screen (so that you do not know which number is hidden).

Now press P to predict the hidden number.

You can now type in your guesses.

1 Play this game several times. Count the number of guesses needed to find the number each time.

Discuss the strategy you use for choosing the next number to guess.

2 Change the game by changing the formula. You could, for example, use one of these formulae:

RND (50)
RND (100)
99 + RND (900)
RND (200) / 10
RND (1000) / 100

If you are using *Spread*

If you are using a graphical calculator

3 Change the game by thinking of the number hidden as being produced by two (or three) dice. You could, for example, try one of these formulae:

RND (6) + RND (6)

RND (6) * RND (6)

RND (6) + RND (6) + RND (6)

You might want to think carefully about the best strategy to use to find the number using as few guesses as possible.

THE BEST STRATEGY

1 When you played the game of guessing a number between 1 and 15, what strategy did you use?

 One way of recording your strategy is to use a tree diagram. Here is how it might work:

Using *this* strategy you need two guesses if the number is 12. You need five guesses if the number is 1.

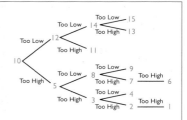

2 (a) Draw a complete tree diagram for *your* strategy for guessing a number between 1 and 15.

(b) Using your strategy, how many guesses are needed if the number is 2?

(c) What is the highest number of guesses you could need using your strategy?

(d) Write down how many guesses you would need for each of the 15 numbers.

(e) What is the mean number of guesses needed when your strategy is used?

3 Answer question 1 for variations of the game.

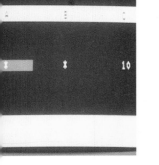

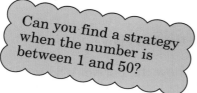

Can you find a strategy when the number is between 1 and 50?

Can you find a strategy when you have decimals?

It's a lot harder when the formula is RND (6) * RND (6)

 Here is a harder version of the game. Someone thinks of two numbers between 1 and 15. They tell you the sum of the numbers. For example if they think of 6 and 4 they tell you the sum is 10. You have to guess what the two numbers are. You have to guess each number in turn. The game might start as shown in the drawing.

As usual, you are told whether each guess is the right number, too high or two low.

You have to guess both numbers using as few guesses as possible.

 You could use *Spread* for this game. You will need 3 columns.

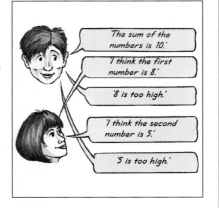

The sum of the numbers is 10.'

'I think the first number is 8.'

'8 is too high.'

'I think the second number is 5.'

'5 is too high.'

C17
page
91

E25
page
152

4 Play this harder game.

Find a good strategy for making the guesses and explain your strategy.

NUMBER CARDS

 Here is a set of cards for a number 'trick'.

Ask someone to choose a number between 1 and 15 but not to tell you what they have chosen.

Now ask them which of these cards the number is on.

A 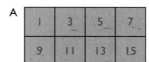 B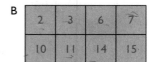

C  D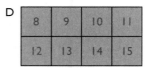

You can find their chosen number by adding the first numbers of the cards they chose.

For example, if they chose 6 they would say it was on cards B and C. You find their chosen number by adding the first numbers on these cards (2 + 4).

1 Try the trick described in the box above.

Discuss with other people how the person who made the cards decided what numbers to put on each card.

2 Design some cards which would work for choosing a number between 1 and 7. How many cards are needed?

3 Design some cards which would work for choosing a number between 1 and 31. How many cards are needed?

4 Do the same for choosing a number between 1 and 50.

5 How many cards would be needed for choosing a number between:

(a) 1 and 63?

(b) 1 and 100?

(c) 1 and 1000?

6 This set of cards can be used when someone chooses a number between 1 and 26. They have to say whether the number is on the card and, if so, what colour the number is.

A

1	2	4	5	7	8
10	11	13	14	16	17
19	20	22	23	25	26

B

3	4	5	6	7	8
12	13	14	15	16	17
21	22	23	24	25	26

C

9	10	11	12	13	14
15	16	17	18	19	20
21	22	23	24	25	26

Use these cards to discover what number someone is thinking of. You will need to practise first, so that you know how to do it.

7 How many two-colour cards would be needed for choosing a number between:

(*a*) 1 and 80?

(*b*) 1 and 1000?

A4
page
34

8 Design some three-colour cards.

FIND ONE NUMBER

1 Someone is thinking of a positive number.

He says: if I call the number *a* then $a^2 + 1 = 50$.

What is the number?

2 What are the answers to these? For some you will need to use a calculator or a computer. If you use *Spread* you could set it up with 11 rows and 2 columns. Enter the formula B = A^2. Then enter blocks of numbers in column *A* and update the table.

(*a*) $a^2 + 1 = 10$ (*b*) $a^2 + 1 = 170$ (*c*) $a^2 + 1 = 530$

(*d*) $a^2 + 1 = 5330$ (*e*) $a^2 + 1 = 20$ (*f*) $a^2 + 1 = 100$

3 Find a positive number for the following.

(*a*) $b^2 - 9 = 160$ (*b*) $c^2 - c = 380$ (*c*) $d(d + 1) = 10$

(*d*) $e(e - 2) = 20$ (*e*) $(f + 1)(f + 2) = 60$ (*f*) $g(g + 1)(g + 2) = 125$

(*g*) $h(h + 1)(h + 2)(h + 3) = 5040$

B12
page
63

COUNTING UP AND COUNTING DOWN

You will need to use *Spread* for this activity.

1 Set up *Spread* with 1 row and 1 column.
Enter the formula *A = A + 2*
Enter the number 6
Keep pressing U until you get 50

2 Repeat question 1. Keep 6 and 50 the same, but use a different formula.

What formulae can be used?

3 Repeat question 2 but choose different numbers instead of 6 and 50.

What formulae can be used?

4 Set up *Spread* with 1 row and 2 columns.
Enter the formula *A = A + 1*
Enter the formula *B = B – 1*
Enter the number 0 in column *A*
Enter the number 100 in column *B*
Keep pressing U until the numbers are the same and then stop.

What number is shown when you stop?

5 Repeat question 4, but this time enter the formula *B = B – 3*.

Predict what number will be shown when you stop. Check your prediction.

6 Repeat question 5, but use different formulae in columns *A* and *B*.

7 Set up *Spread* with 1 row and 2 columns.
Enter the formula *A = A + 2*
Enter the formula *B = B + 4*
Enter the number 70 in column *A*
Enter the number 30 in column *B*
Keep pressing U until the numbers are the same and then stop.

What number is shown when you stop?

8 Repeat question 7, but use different formulae in columns *A* and *B*.

Which pairs of formulae can be used?

Try to predict the stopping number for each pair of formulae.

9 Explore this situation further.

A4
page
34

C17
page
91

You could use different starting numbers.

You could use three columns instead of two.

You could change the rule for stopping.

FIND TWO NUMBERS

1 Someone is thinking of two numbers. She is asked to give you a clue about what the numbers are.

'If I call my numbers X and Y then X + Y = 10.'

(a) What could the numbers be? Write down several answers.

(b) She now tells you something else about the same two numbers.

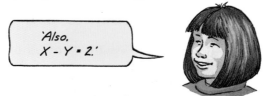

'Also, X – Y = 2.'

What could the two numbers be now?

2 (a) You do not know what the numbers p and q are.

'I will tell you that p + 2q = 24.'

What could p and q be?

(b)

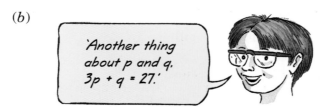

'Another thing about p and q, 3p + q = 27.'

What could p and q be now?

3 You do not know what the numbers c and d are.

'I'll tell you that c + 4d = 18.'

You still do not know what c and d are. But you could make some statements about c and d, based on what you have been told.

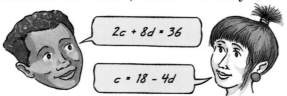

2c + 8d = 36

c = 18 – 4d

Make some more statements about c and d.

■ **4** You do not know what *a* and *b* are.

Somebody tells you two statements about *a* and *b*.

a + 3*b* = 26

2*a* – *b* = 17

(*a*) Use them to make some more statements about *a* and *b*.

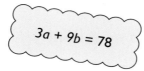

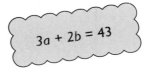

(*b*) Discuss with other people how these two statements have been produced.

(*c*) Now look at these two statements about *a* and *b*.

a + 3*b* = 26
6*a* – 3*b* = 51

By adding these two statements you can get this statement:

7*a* = 77

What does this tell you about *a*? And *b*?

■ **5** For each of the following:
 (i) write down some more statements about the two numbers
 (ii) find the two numbers.

(*a*) *a* + *b* = 10   (*b*) 2*c* – *d* = 23   (*c*) *e* + *f* = 30   (*d*) 2*g* + *h* = 43
   2*a* – 3*b* = 5   *c* + 2*d* = 29   *e* + 2*f* = 40   *g* + 2*h* = 47

(*e*) 5*j* + 4*k* = 24   (*f*) 3*m* + *n* = 30, *n* = 2*m*   (*g*) 3*p* – 7*q* = 100, *p* = 4*q*
   3*j* + 6*k* = 27

■ **6** Find the three numbers.

(*a*) *a* + *b* + *c* = 20, *a* = 2*b*, *b* = 3*c*

(*b*) 2*e* + 3*f* + *g* = 26, 2*e* + 3*f* + 4*g* = 47, 2*e* – 3*f* = 1

B12
page
63

YOU COULD USE . . .

An alternative way of answering questions 5 and 6 in *Find two numbers* is to use *Spread*.

For example, to answer question 5 (*a*) you could set up *Spread* with several rows and 4 columns. Enter the formulae *C* = *A* + *B* and *D* = 2*A* – 3*B*.

Try different numbers in columns *A* and *B* until you get 10 in column *C* and 5 in column *D* at the same time.

BAGS OF CUBES

■ 1 Here are two bags.

There are *r* cubes in the red bag and *b* cubes in the blue bag.

There are seven more cubes in the red bag than in the blue bag.

The total number of the cubes in the two bags is 49.

Write down some statements about *r* and *b*.

Find the number of cubes in each bag.

■ 2 Here are three bags.

There are *y* cubes in the yellow bag, *g* cubes in the green bag and *p* cubes in the purple bag.

The total number of cubes in the three bags is 50.

If the cubes in the purple bag were tipped into the yellow bag there would be two more cubes in the yellow bag than in the green bag.

If you doubled the number of cubes in the yellow bag, and trebled the number of cubes in the purple bag there would be 84 cubes in the three bags altogether.

Find the number of cubes in each bag.

■ 3 Here are four bags.

The total number of cubes in the bags is 340.

There are 44 more cubes in the orange bag than in the yellow and blue bags put together.

The number of cubes in each of the bags is a power of 2.

How many cubes are there in each bag?

■ 4 Make up your own problems about bags of cubes.

Give them to someone else to solve.

REVIEW EXERCISES B

1 Simplify the following expressions:

(a) $x + x + 6$

(b) $2a + 3a$

(c) $s + 2 + 3s + 4$

(d) $2a + 5b + 7a + 8b$

(e) $2a + 3b + c + 7a + 3c$

2 Write down an expression for the perimeter of each of these shapes and simplify it.

(a)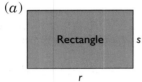

(b)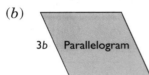

(c)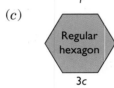

(d)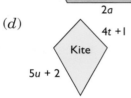

3 (a) $2P + 1$ and $2Q + 1$ are two odd numbers.

What is the sum of these two odd numbers? What does this tell you about the sum of two odd numbers?

(b) $2N + 1$, $2N + 3$, $2N + 5$, $2N + 7$, $2N + 9$ are five consecutive odd numbers. What is their sum? What does this tell you about the sum of five consecutive odd numbers?

4 Simplify the following expressions:

(a) $2x - 4x$

(b) $3y - 7y$

(c) $2a + b + 3a - 4b$

(d) $p - 3q - 5p - 7q$

(e) $3x - 2y - 3 - 4x + 5y - 7$

(f) $mn + 2mn$

(g) $ab + c + 2ab + 4c$

(h) $xy + yz + xz + 2xy + 3xz + 5yz$

(i) $2s + 3t + 4st - 6s$

5 Simplify the following expressions:

(a) $3d^2 + 4d^2$

(b) $a^2 + 2b^2 + 3b^2$

(c) $2p^2 + 2q^2 + 3p^2 - 5q^2$

(d) $x^2 + 4x + 6x + 7x^2$

(e) $6d^2 + 5d + 1 + 8d^2$

6 Find the surface areas of these cuboids

(a)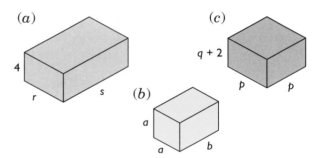

(b)

(c)

> **I** Look at these examples. If you do not understand them discuss them with someone else.
>
> $4x \times 3x = 12x^2$
> $3x^2 \times 2x^3 = 6x^5$
> $8x^3 \div 2x^2 = 4x$

7 Simplify the following expressions:

(a) $2a \times 4a$

(b) $3z \times 5z$

(c) $4c^2 \times 2c$

(d) $5d^3 \times 4d^4$

(e) $4p^5 \div 2p^3$

(f) $10q^2 \div 5q$

(g) $12r^4 \div 4r^4$

(h) $10e^2 \div 5e^2$

(i) $6s^3 \div 6s^3$

(j) $(3a^3)^2$

EXERCISE 8 Using Formulae

1 Triangles are made by joining up a number of dots as shown.

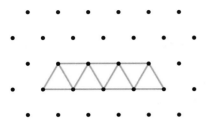

This formula gives the number of triangles made by joining D dots.

$D - 2$

(a) How many triangles are there if there are 8 dots?

(b) How many triangles are there if there are 80 dots?

2 This formula gives the number of matches needed to make a row of N squares.

$3N + 1$

(a) How many matches are needed to make a row of 10 squares?

(b) How many matches are needed to make a row of 13 squares?

3 This formula gives the number of matches needed to make a double-row of squares.

$5N + 2$

(a) How many matches are needed to make a double-row 10 squares long?

(b) How many matches are needed to make a double-row 13 squares long?

4 A structure of cardboard compartments is made in the form of a cuboid. Each compartment is a cube with side length 4 cm.

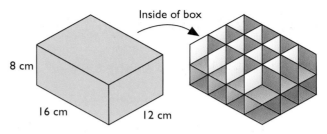

$P = 4, Q = 3, R = 2$

This formula gives the area in square centimetres of the card needed to make a structure of P by Q by R compartments.

$48PQR + 16PQ + 16QR + 16PR$

(a) Find the area of card needed to make a structure of 2 by 2 by 2 compartments.

(b) Find the area of card needed to make a structure of 3 by 4 by 5 compartments.

5 A triangle of matches is made like this.

If the triangle has R rows the number of matches needed is

$\frac{1}{2}(3R^2 + 3R)$

(a) How many matches are needed for a triangle with 3 rows?

(b) How many matches are needed for a triangle with 17 rows?

6 (a) A structure is made of four wooden cubes stacked on the floor.

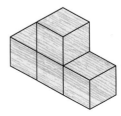

If s is the length of the side of one of the cubes the total surface area of wood visible is $15s^2$

What area of wood is visible if:

(i) The side length of a cube is 2 m?

(ii) The side length of a cube is 0.5 m?

(iii) The side length of a cube is 1.3 m?

(b) A bigger structure is now made from 9 cubes, as shown.

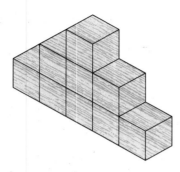

(i) Find a formula for the total surface area of wood visible.

(ii) What area of wood is visible if s is 0.7 m?

■ **7** A ball is thrown upwards. When the height of the ball is h metres above the starting point, the velocity of the ball is $\sqrt{200 - 20h}$ ms^{-1}

(a) What is the velocity of the ball when $h = 4.3$?

(b) What is the velocity of the ball when $h = 10$?

(c) What is the velocity of the ball when $h = -5.6$?

(d) Explain the meaning of the answers to (b) and (c).

■ **8** The formula in question 1 for the number of triangles formed from D dots is $T = D - 2$

Rearrange this formula so that it is a formula for the number of dots:

$D = ...$

■ **9** The formulae in questions 2 and 3 for the number of matches needed are $M = 3N + 1$ and $M = 5N + 2$.

Rearrange both these formulae in the form

$N = ...$

■ **10** The formula in question 4 for the area of cardboard is
$A = 48PQR + 16PQ + 16QR + 16PR$

(a) Rearrange this formula in the form $P = ...$

(b) Now rearrange the formula in the form $Q = ...$

■ **11** The time T in seconds, taken for a pendulum of length L metres to complete one swing (backwards and forwards) is

$T = 2\pi\sqrt{\frac{L}{10}}$

(a) A pendulum is 1 metre long. Find the time for one complete swing.

(b) A pendulum is 30 cm long. How many complete swings will it make in a minute?

(c) What is the length of a pendulum which makes one complete swing every second?

EXERCISE 9 Pythagoras' Theorem

1 The isosceles triangle ABC has sides of length 34 cm, 34 cm and 32 cm. AM is the line of symmetry.

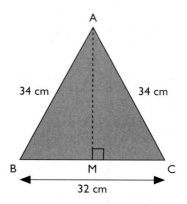

(a) Find the length of AM.

(b) Find the area of the triangle.

2 The area of a rhombus is 840 cm². The length of one of its diagonals is 40 cm.

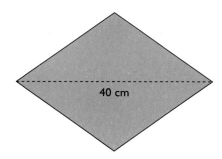

(a) Find the length of the other diagonal.

(b) Find the perimeter of the rhombus.

3 The diagonals of a kite are both 24 cm long.

Two of the sides of the kite are 13 cm long.

Find the lengths of the other two sides.

4

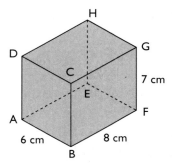

In the cuboid shown above, find the distance of vertex A from each of the other seven vertices.

EXERCISE 10 **Estimating and Approximating**

1 Answer this question without using a calculator. Pick out the right answer for each of the following:

(a) 198 + 197 = 295 or 305 or 395

(b) 23 + 24 + 27 + 28 = 72 or 82 or 102

(c) 1234 − 885 = 349 or 389 or 439

(d) 43.27 + 12.93 = 55.2 or 56.2 or 57.2

(e) 9.13 + 0.095 = 9.225 or 10.005 or 11.005

(f) 23 × 24 = 392 or 552 or 732

(g) 501 × 513 = 25643 or 256043 or 257013

(h) 34.2 × 23.4 = 80.028 or 800.28 or 8002.8

(i) 534 × 0.0437 = 2.33358 or 23.3358 or 233.358

(j) 347 ÷ 43 = 8.070 or 9.070 or 10.070

(k) 55.5 ÷ 0.056 = 89.11 or 991.1 or 1001.1

2 In this question give all your answers to a sensible degree of accuracy.

(a) Ann measures one side of a cardboard regular hexagon as 6.7 cm. Find the perimeter of the hexagon.

(b) David measures the length and width of a cardboard rectangle as 8.7 cm and 4.6 cm. Find the area of the rectangle.

(c) Jenny measures the diameter of a circular pond as 6 m. Find the area of the pond.

(d) 850 envelopes are to be sent out with identical contents. The weight of one envelope is measured as 53 g. What is the total weight of the envelopes in kilograms?

(e) A side of a square is measured as 570 mm. Find the area of the square in square metres.

3 Here is a set of times recorded by three experimenters for an experiment.

4.3 secs, 5.4 secs, 3.5 secs, 6.1 secs, 4.0 secs, 5.42 secs, 3.48 secs, 4.02 secs, 4.97 secs, 4.09 secs, 3.4 secs, 4.2 secs, 2.6 secs, 3.9 secs, 6.0 secs.

(a) One of the experimenters gave her times more accurately than the other two. Correct her times so that they are to the same degree of accuracy as the other times.

(b) Which of the 15 times is the largest? Look at how accurately this time has been given. What is the highest value it could actually have been?

(c) What is the lowest value the smallest time could actually have been?

EXERCISE 11 Scatter Graphs and Frequency Distributions

1 Some people do 'bike jumping' on BMX bikes.

This table shows the height of jumps for different weights of bike in one set of experiments.

Weight (kg)	Height (cm)
8.0	26.8
8.5	26.4
9.0	26.1
9.5	25.7
10.0	25.0
10.5	24.8
11.0	24.3

(a) Draw a scatter graph to show these results.

(b) Draw a line of best fit.

(c) Predict the height for a bike weighing 9.7 kg.

2 This cumulative frequency curve shows the percentage of men achieving particular heights (measured in mm).

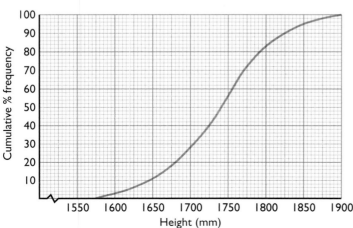

(a) Use the graph to find the median height for men.

(b) Find the 5th and 95th percentiles.

(c) The doorway on a garden shed is 1.63 metres high. What percentage of men would have to duck their heads to go into the shed?

(d)

FRANKIE'S NIGHT CLUB
Bouncer needed.
Must be at least 6 feet tall

What percentage of men are tall enough for the job?

(There are about 2.54 cm in an inch and 12 inches in a foot.)

3 Furniture designers use knee heights to help them decide how high school tables should be. Here are knee height measurements for children aged between 8 and 11. The measurements are correct to the nearest 10 mm.

Knee height	Percentage
$340 \leq k < 360$	1
$360 \leq k < 380$	4
$380 \leq k < 400$	9
$400 \leq k < 420$	13
$420 \leq k < 440$	23
$440 \leq k < 460$	21
$460 \leq k < 480$	16
$480 \leq k < 500$	9
$500 \leq k < 520$	4

Give all your answers to a sensible degree of accuracy.

(a) Find the mean knee height for children aged between 8 and 11.

(b) Draw a cumulative percentage frequency curve for the knee height data.

(c) Use your curve to find the median knee height for children aged between 8 and 11. Compare this with the mean knee height you obtained for part (a).

(d) Find the interquartile range.

(e) Find the 5th and 95th percentiles.

(f) A table used by this age group has an overall height of 600 mm and the thickness of the top is 40 mm. Is it suitable?

(g) A particular school had to move a junior class into an infant classroom one day because of a radiator leak. The tables in the infant classroom had an overall height of 500 mm and the top was 40 mm thick. Estimate the percentage of the junior class who could not get their legs under the table.

EXERCISE 12 Equations

1 Solve the following equations:

(a) $x + 5 = 12$

(b) $3y = 18$

(c) $4z = 10$

(d) $a - 7 = 14$

(e) $2b + 3 = 19$

(f) $4d + 17 = 93$

(g) $5p - 83 = 177$

2 Solve the following equations:

(a) $6x + 2 = 17$

(b) $5r - 14 = 29$

(c) $7N - 3 = 20$

(d) $5b + 10 = 5$

(e) $3c - 7 = -13$

(f) $4z + 22 = 8$

3 Solve the following equations.

(a) $3x + 2 = 2x + 5$

(b) $5y - 7 = 13 - 3y$

(c) $3(z + 5) = 24$

(d) $4(a - 1) + 5(a + 1) = 100$

(e) $7(b + 3) = 45 - 3(12 - b)$

4 Solve the following pairs of equations simultaneously:

(a) $2a + 3b = 12$
$a + b = 5$

(b) $3r + 2s = 25$
$3r - 2s = 17$

(c) $2p + 3q = 43$
$3p + 2q = 47$

(d) $r + 3s = 5$
$4r + 7s = 10$

(e) $4z + 3w = 13$
$2z + 4w = 17$

5 Ann is x years old. In five years time her father will be twice as old as her.

(a) How old is her father now?

(b) 13 years from now the sum of their ages will be 100. How old will Ann be then?

6 Solve these equations. Each equation has two solutions. For some equations one of the solutions is a negative number.

(a) $x^2 + 11 = 300$

(b) $y^2 + 11 = 13\,700$

(c) $a^2 + 5 = 100$

(d) $b^2 - 5 = 200$

(e) $d(d + 1) = 1406$

(f) $e(e - 1) = 2406$

(g) $a^2 - 6a + 5 = 0$

(h) $b^2 - 6b - 4 = 0$

7 ANGLES, POLYGONS AND CIRCLES

PARALLEL SIDES

You might find the resource sheet *Shapes* helpful.

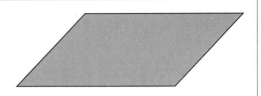

I A parallelogram is a quadrilateral with two pairs of parallel sides.

1 How many pairs of parallel sides does each of the following quadrilaterals have?

(*a*) A square   (*b*) A rectangle   (*c*) A rhombus

(*d*) A trapezium   (*e*) A kite

2 (*a*) Which of the shapes in question 1 have two angles which are equal?

(*b*) Which of the shapes in question 1 have two angles which add up to 180°?

3 (*a*) Draw a pentagon with one pair of parallel sides.

(*b*) Can a pentagon have two pairs of parallel sides? If so, draw a pentagon to illustrate.

4 (*a*) Draw a hexagon with one pair of parallel sides.

(*b*) Can a hexagon have more than one pair of parallel sides? If so, draw hexagons to illustrate.

5 Can a triangle have a pair of parallel sides?

6 How many parallel sides can a polygon with 4 sides have? What about a polygon with 5 sides? With 6 sides? With 7 sides? . . .

A1 page 32

Draw sketches to explain your answers. Show on the sketches which angles are equal and which angles add up to 180°.

STARS

1 Here is a regular 5-pointed star drawn inside a circle.

(*a*) Find the angle at each point of the star.

(*b*) What is the sum of the angles at all five points?

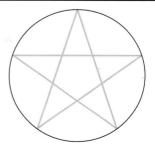

2 Draw some different five-pointed stars inside a circle. You can put the points where you like on the circle.

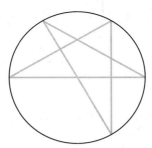

Measure the angles of the points. What can be said about the angles this time?

3 Draw some five pointed stars not inside a circle.

Measure the angles of the points. What happens this time?

4 Investigate the angles of the points of stars with different numbers of points.

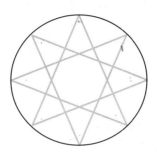

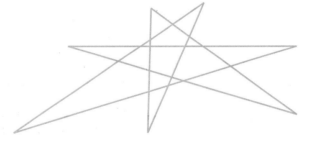

C13
page
88

INSIDE A POLYGON

You will find squared paper useful for questions 1 to 3.

I Here is a square drawn inside a square. The corners of the inside square touch the outside square.

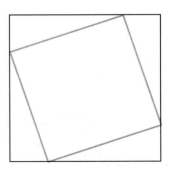

1 (*a*) Draw a square.

(*b*) Draw several squares inside it. The corners of these inside squares should touch the outside square (like the square in the box).

(*c*) Which inside square is the smallest?

2 (*a*) Draw a square.

   (*b*) Draw several rectangles inside the square. The corners of the rectangle should all touch the square.

   (*c*) How do you make such a rectangle as small as possible?

   (*d*) How do you make such a rectangle as big as possible?

3 Which of these shapes can be drawn inside a square, with all their corners touching the square?

   (*a*) Rhombus   (*b*) Kite

   (*c*) Trapezium   (*d*) Parallelogram

> You will find isometric paper useful for questions 4 to 6.

4 Here is an equilateral triangle drawn inside an equilateral triangle. The corners of the inside equilateral triangle touch the outside equilateral triangle.

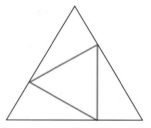

   (*a*) Draw an equilateral triangle.

   (*b*) Draw several equilateral triangles inside it. The corners of these inside equilateral triangles should touch the outside equilateral triangle.

   (*c*) Which inside equilateral triangle is the smallest?

5 Investigate equilateral triangles inside a regular hexagon.

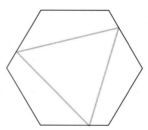

6 Investigate regular hexagons inside an equilateral triangle.

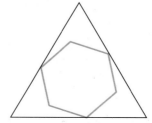

C14
page
88

66

THE ROD AND THE HANDKERCHIEF

 A metre rod has a handkerchief tied at its centre.

Two people hold the rod. One person is at each end.

You might be able to answer some of these questions by just thinking about them. For other questions you might need to draw accurate pictures.

1 Two people are holding the rod in the box above.

One person stays still. The other person moves around the still person.

What is the locus (path) of the handkerchief?

2 Two parallel lines are drawn on the ground. The distance between the lines is equal to the length of the rod.

The two people carrying the rod walk along the lines.

What is the locus of the handkerchief?

3 Two parallel lines are drawn on the ground. The distance between the lines is less than the length of the rod.

The two people carrying the rod walk along the lines.

What is the locus of the handkerchief?

4 Two lines are drawn on the ground at right angles to each other.

The two people carrying the rod walk along the lines.

What is the locus of the handkerchief?

(You might be able to explain why this happens after you have answered question 1 on page 67.)

5 A circle is drawn on the ground.

The two people carrying the rod walk along the circle.

What is the locus of the handkerchief?

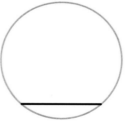

6 Suppose the radius of the circle the people walk around in question 5 is 2 m. What is the area of the space *between* the locus and the circle?

(Remember that the rod is a metre rod.)

Now try using circles of different sizes.

What do you notice about your answers for the circles of different sizes?

You will need to use Pythagoras' theorem for question 6.

7 A square is drawn on the ground.

The two people carrying the rod walk along the square.

What is the locus of the handkerchief?

8 Suppose the square they walk around has sides of length 2 m. What is the area of the space *between* the locus and the square?

Now try using squares of different sizes.

What do you notice about your answers for the squares of different sizes?

9 Someone moves the handkerchief so that it is no longer at the centre of the rod.

C15
page
90

Answer questions 1 to 8 again now that the handkerchief is no longer at the centre. (You can decide exactly where the handkerchief is.)

INSIDE AND OUTSIDE A CIRCLE

1 Draw a circle. Draw a diameter.

Draw several angles on this diameter.

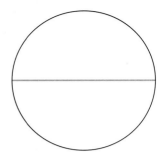

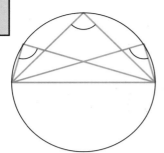

Measure the angles.
What do you notice?

2 Draw a circle. Mark two points on the circle.

Draw several angles from these two points.

Measure the angles. What do you notice?

3 (*a*) Draw a circle.
Draw an angle of 60° in the circle.

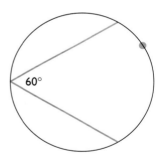

Now choose a point on the opposite side to the 60° angle, as shown in the drawing.

Join up the points like this.

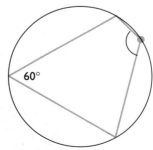

Measure the new angle. What do you notice?

(*b*) What do you think would happen if you did the same thing again but chose a different angle instead of 60°?

Try it and see if you were right.

4 Draw a circle of radius 5 cm. Draw a triangle inside the circle. The angles of the triangle are to be 90°, 40° and 50°.

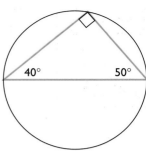

5 Draw a circle of radius 5 cm. Draw a triangle inside the circle. The angles of the triangle are to be 70°, 70° and 40°.

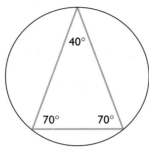

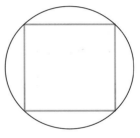

6 Draw a circle of radius 5 cm. Draw a triangle inside it with angles of 50°, 60° and 70°.

7 A square can be drawn inside a circle (with all its corners on the circle).

Which of the following quadrilaterals can be drawn inside a circle?

(*a*) Rectangle   (*b*) Rhombus   (*c*) Parallelogram

(*d*) Kite   (*e*) Trapezium

8 A square can be drawn outside a circle (with each of its sides touching the circle).

Which of the following quadrilaterals can be drawn outside a circle?

(*a*) Rectangle   (*b*) Rhombus   (*c*) Parallelogram

(*d*) Kite   (*e*) Trapezium

9 A circle can be drawn both inside and outside a square.

Investigate what other quadrilaterals are like a square in this way.

Investigate what hexagons are like a square in this way.

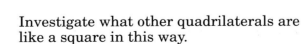

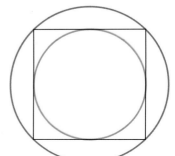

C14
page
88

71

8 WINDOWS

WINDOWS ON NUMBER GRIDS

You need the resource sheet *Number grids* for this activity.

I

1	2	3	4	5	6	7	8	9	10
11	12	13	14	15	16	17	18	19	20
21	22	23	24	25	26	27	28	29	30
31	32	33	34	35	36	37	38	39	40
41	42	43	44	45	46	47	48	49	50
51	52	53	54	55	56	57	58	59	60
61	62	63	64	65	66	67	68	69	70
71	72	73	74	75	76	77	78	79	80
81	82	83	84	85	86	87	88	89	90
91	92	93	94	95	96	97	98	99	100

1	2	3	4	5	6	7	8	9	10
11	12	13	14	15	16	17	18	19	20
21	22	23	24	25	26	27	28	29	30
31	32	33	34	35	36	37	38	39	40
41	42	43	44	45	46	47	48	49	50
51	52	53	54	55	56	57	58	59	60
61	62	63	64	65	66	67	68	69	70
71	72	73	74	75	76	77	78	79	80
81	82	83	84	85	86	87	88	89	90
91	92	93	94	95	96	97	98	99	100

The picture on the left is a number grid containing the numbers 1 to 100.

The picture on the right shows part of this number grid seen through a window.

Four numbers are visible through the window.

1 Look at the window in the box above.

(*a*) Add both pairs of the numbers in opposite corners:

$$17 + 28$$
$$\text{and } 18 + 27$$

(*b*) What do you notice?

(*c*) Move the window somewhere else on the grid. Do the same as before.

(*d*) What do you notice?

(*e*) Try to explain why this happens.

2 Look at the window in the box above.

(*a*) Multiply both pairs of numbers in opposite corners:

$$17 \times 28$$
$$\text{and } 18 \times 27$$

(*b*) What do you notice?

(*c*) Move the window somewhere else on the grid. Do the same as before.

(*d*) What do you notice?

(*e*) Try to explain why this happens.

53	54	55
63	64	65
73	74	75

3 Use a bigger window.

Answer questions 1 and 2 for this bigger window.

4 Try some other windows.

68	69
78	79
88	89

52	53	54	55
62	63	64	65
72	73	74	75
82	83	84	85

17	18
27	28

5 Here is the first window again. The sum of the numbers in this window is 90.

What happens to the sum of the numbers when you move this window around?

The table shows the smallest number and the sum of the numbers for different positions of this window.

Smallest number	Sum
13	74
14	78
15	82
16	86
17	90

When the smallest number goes up by 1 the sum goes up by 4. Here is a rule for finding the sum if you know the smallest number.

SUM = 4 × SMALLEST NUMBER + 22

This could also be written as

$s = 4n + 22$

6 Use the formula in the box above to find the sum if the smallest number is

(a) 6   (b) 22   (c) 47   (d) 89

7 How could you find the smallest number if you know the sum? Find the smallest number if the sum is

(a) 34   (b) 58   (c) 154   (d) 326

You might want to use algebra to help you answer question 9.

8 Write down a formula which you could use to find the smallest number if you know the sum.

9 Explain why the formula for the 2 by 2 window is $s = 4n + 22$.

73

■ **10** The formula *s* = *4n* + *22* only works for a 2 by 2 square window.

A window of a different shape or size would need a different formula.

Find a window for each of these formulae:

(*a*) *s* = *6n* + *36*

(*b*) *s* = *4n* + *15*

(*c*) *s* = *5n* + *50*

■ **11** Make up some windows of your own. You could use the windows shown below, but you do not have to.

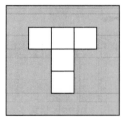 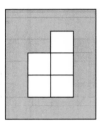

Find the formula for each of your windows.

B7
page
58

Give someone else your formulae. See if they can find which windows you used.

QUICK WAYS OF FINDING SUMS

1 Look at this window.

32	33	34
42	43	44
52	53	54

You need the resource sheet *Number grids* for this activity.

(*a*) Find the sum of the 9 numbers in the window.

(*b*) Multiply the middle number in the window by 9.

(*c*) What do you notice?

2 Move the window in question 1 to a different position on the grid. Find the sum of the numbers in the window. Multiply the middle number by 9. What do you notice?

Try several different positions for the window.

■ Explain why the result works.

3 Try the same idea with different shaped windows, such as those shown here.

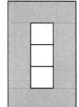

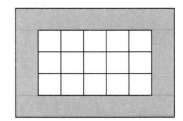

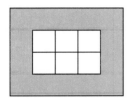

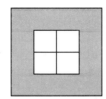

4 Try using windows where at least one of the dimensions is even. You will need to adapt the idea in question 1.

5 Try using symmetrical windows which are not rectangles.

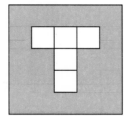

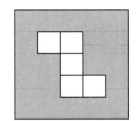

WINDOWS ON TABLES GRIDS

You need the resource sheet *Tables grids* for this activity.

1 Here is a 2 by 2 window onto a tables grid.

1	2	3	4	5	6	7	8	9	10
2	4	6	8	10	12	14	16	18	20
3	6	9	12	15	18	21	24	27	30
4	8	12	16	20	24	28	32	36	40
5	10	15	20	25	30	35	40	45	50
6	12	18	24	30	36	42	48	54	60
7	14	21	28	35	42	49	56	63	70
8	16	24	32	40	48	56	64	72	80
9	18	27	36	45	54	63	72	81	90
10	20	30	40	50	60	70	80	90	100

1	2	3	4	5	6	7	8	9	10
2	4	6	8	10	12	14	16	18	20
3	6	9	12	15	18	21	24	27	30
4	8	12	16	20	24	28	32	36	40
5	10	15	20	25	30	35	40	45	50
6	12	18	24	30	36	42	48	54	60
7	14	21	28	35	42	49	56	63	70
8	16	24	32	40	48	56	64	72	80
9	18	27	36	45	54	63	72	81	90
10	20	30	40	50	60	70	80	90	100

(*a*) Two of the numbers in this window are consecutive. Move this window around the grid. Find other positions for this window where two of the numbers are consecutive.

(*b*) Describe how to position the window so that two numbers shown in the window are consecutive.

(c) Use algebra to explain why these positions of the windows show consecutive numbers.

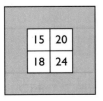

2 In this window two of the numbers differ by 2.

(*a*) Describe where to find other positions of this window where two numbers differ by 2.

(*b*) Use algebra to explain your results.

(*c*) Where do two numbers differ by 3? Or 4? Or . . .

C16 page 91

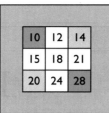

3 Here is a 3 by 3 window onto the tables grid.

Here are some relationships between some of the numbers in this window.

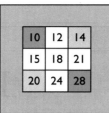

$10 + 28 - 14 - 20 = 4$

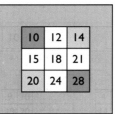

$10 \times 28 = 14 \times 20$

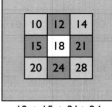

$12 + 15 + 21 + 24$
$= 10 + 14 + 20 + 28$

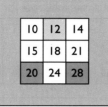

$20 + 28 = 4 \times 12$

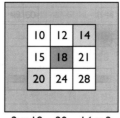

$2 \times 18 - 20 - 14 = 2$

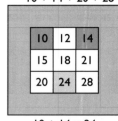

$10 + 14 = 24$

(a) What happens to each of these relationships when the window is moved somewhere else on the grid?

(b) Explain some of the relationships. You might want to use algebra.

4 (a) Use a window of a different size to the window in question 2. Discover some relationships of your own for the numbers in your window.

(b) What happens to the relationships when your window is moved somewhere else on the grid?

(c) Explain some of the relationships. You might want to use algebra.

5 The mean of the numbers in this window is 35.

(a) Find the mean of the numbers in square or rectangular windows of other sizes.

(b) Use algebra to prove any general patterns you discover.

6 (a) Find the mean of the numbers in symmetrical windows which are not rectangular.

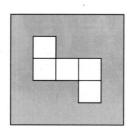

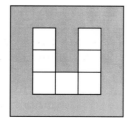

(b) Use algebra to prove any general patterns you discover.

BIGGER AND BIGGER WINDOWS

You need the resource sheet Number grids for this activity.

1 Here is a set of windows on a number grid.

1	2	3	4	5	6	7	8	9	10
11	12	13	14	15	16	17	18	19	20
21	22	23	24	25	26	27	28	29	30
31	32	33	34	35	36	37	38	39	40
41	42	43	44	45	46	47	48	49	50
51	52	53	54	55	56	57	58	59	60
61	62	63	64	65	66	67	68	69	70
71	72	73	74	75	76	77	78	79	80
81	82	83	84	85	86	87	88	89	90
91	92	93	94	95	96	97	98	99	100

In this window the sum of the numbers on yellow squares is 202. The sum of the numbers on blue squares is 606.

(a) Find the sum of the numbers on the green squares. Find the sum of the numbers on the red squares.

(b) Predict the next three numbers in the number sequence.

(c) Continue the pattern to check your predictions. How do you make your predictions work when you reach the edge of the grid?

(d) Explain why you get this number pattern.

2 Move the rings of squares somewhere else on the grid. What happens to the number pattern?

3 Start with a rectangle instead of a square. You can use rectangles of different sizes.

1	2	3	4	5	6	7	8	9	10
11	12	13	14	15	16	17	18	19	20
21	22	23	24	25	26	27	28	29	30
31	32	33	34	35	36	37	38	39	40
41	42	43	44	45	46	47	48	49	50
51	52	53	54	55	56	57	58	59	60
61	62	63	64	65	66	67	68	69	70
71	72	73	74	75	76	77	78	79	80
81	82	83	84	85	86	87	88	89	90
91	92	93	94	95	96	97	98	99	100

1	2	3	4	5	6	7	8	9	10
11	12	13	14	15	16	17	18	19	20
21	22	23	24	25	26	27	28	29	30
31	32	33	34	35	36	37	38	39	40
41	42	43	44	45	46	47	48	49	50
51	52	53	54	55	56	57	58	59	60
61	62	63	64	65	66	67	68	69	70
71	72	73	74	75	76	77	78	79	80
81	82	83	84	85	86	87	88	89	90
91	92	93	94	95	96	97	98	99	100

4 Start with a different design for your windows. You must decide what rules you use for continuing the geometrical pattern.

	46	
55	56	57
	66	

23	24	25
	34	
	44	

27	
37	
47	48

F33 page 187

OTHER GRIDS

Use any of the ideas from the earlier activities on some new grids such as these.

You need isometric paper or squared paper for this activity.

12	14	16	18	20	22	24	26	28	30
11	13	15	17	19	21	23	25	27	29
10	12	14	16	18	20	22	24	26	28
9	11					21	23	25	27
8	10		14	16		20	22	24	26
7	9		13	15		19	21	23	25
6	8		12	14		18	20	22	24
5	7					17	19	21	23
4	6	8	10	12	14	16	18	20	22
3	5	7	9	11	13	15	17	19	21

55	64	72	79	85	90	94	97	99	100
45	54	63	71	78	84	89	93	96	98
36	44	53	62	70	77	83	88	92	95
28	35	43	52	61	69	76	82	87	91
21					60	68	75	81	86
15		26	33		50	59	67	74	80
10		19	25		40	49	58	66	73
6					31	39	48	57	65
3	5	8	12	17	23	30	38	47	56
1	2	4	7	11	16	22	29	37	46

1									
2	3								
4	5	6							
7									
11		13	14						
16		18	19		21				
22					27	28			
29	30	31	32	33	34	35	36		
37	38	39	40	41	42	43	44	45	
46	47	48	49	50	51	52	53	54	55

Isometric hexagonal grid (numbers 1–96):

Row: 1 2 — 6 7 8 9
Row: 10 11 14 17 18 19 20
Row: 21 22 25 26 27 30 31 32 33
Row: 34 35 36 44 45 46 47 48
Row: 49 50 51 52 53 54 55 56 57 58 59 60 61 62 63
Row: 64 65 66 67 68 69 70 71 72 73 74 75 76
Row: 77 78 79 80 81 82 83 84 85 86 87
Row: 88 89 90 91 92 93 94 95 96

Isometric triangular grid (numbers 1–64):

1
2 3 4
5 6
10 11 14 15 16
17 18 19 22 23 24
26 27 28 29 30 36
37 38 39 40 41 42 43 44 45 46 47 48 49
50 51 52 53 54 55 56 57 58 59 60 61 62 63 64

FIBONACCI WINDOWS

■ 1 Here is a strip grid.

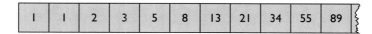

Here is a window on this grid.

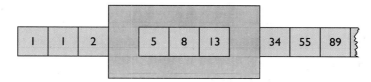

In this window 8^2 is one less than 13×5.

Try moving this window along the grid. What do you find?

Use algebra to explain your findings. To do this you might find it helpful to consider what happens if you move the window one place.

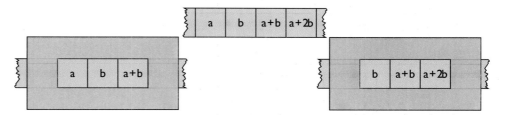

[Hint: Simplify these two expressions: $b^2 - a(a + b)$ and $(a + b)^2 - b(a + 2b)$. Then compare your two answers.]

■ 2 Here is a different window on the same grid.

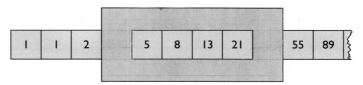

In this window 8×13 is one less than 5×21.

Try moving this window along the grid. What do you find?

Use algebra to explain your findings.

■ 3 Answer questions 1 and 2 for different windows.

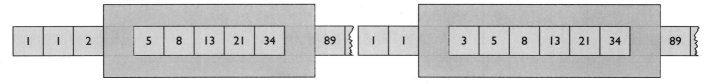

Or for a different strip pattern.

| 2 | 5 | 7 | 12 | 19 |

| 1 | 4 | 5 | 9 | 14 |

F33
page
187

9 WHAT IS TRIGONOMETRY?

COSINES

For this activity you will need the resource sheet *Right-angled triangles*.

You could use *Spread* for the tables in this activity.

I There are five right-angled triangles on the resource sheet with an angle of 40°. The approximate lengths of two of the sides of each triangle are listed in this table. (The longest side of a right-angled triangle is called the **hypotenuse**.)

A (cm)	H (cm)	$\frac{A}{H}$
3.1	4.0	0.775
3.8	5.0	0.76
4.6	6.0	
5.4	7.0	
6.1	8.0	

Table 1

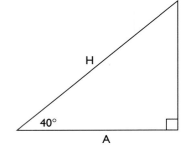

■ **1** Copy and complete the table in the box above.

I The value of $\frac{A}{H}$ is approximately the same for each triangle. If the triangles could be measured exactly you would find that the value of $\frac{A}{H}$ is exactly the same for each triangle. This value is called the **cosine** of 40°, or cos 40°.

■ **2** (a) Decide on a best value of $\frac{A}{H}$ for the set of five triangles in table 1. Give your answer to a sensible degree of accuracy.

(b) Find out how to get cos 40° on your calculator. Write down cos 40° to the same degree of accuracy which you used for (a).

(c) Compare your answers to (a) and (b).

■ **3** This table describes some more right-angled triangles with an angle of 40°.

A (cm)	H (cm)	$\frac{A}{H} = \cos 40°$
5.0	6.53	0.766
	9.0	0.766
8.0		0.766
	10.5	0.766
6.34		0.766

Copy and complete this table.

As you can see from table 1 and the table in question 3:

If you know the **hypotenuse**, to get the other **side next to** the 40° angle you *multiply* by cos 40°.

To get the **hypotenuse**, if you know the other **side next to** the 40° angle you *divide* by cos 40°.

■ **4** (*a*) Choose the right-angled triangles on the resource sheet which have an angle of 30°.

(*b*) For each of these triangles measure the two sides which are next to the angle of 30°.

(*c*) Make a table of results like table 1.

(*d*) Find a best value of $\frac{A}{H}$ for the whole set of triangles.

(*e*) Find cos 30° on your calculator.

(*f*) Compare your answers to (*d*) and (*e*).

■ **5** Find the side marked with a question mark for each of these triangles.

(*a*)

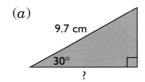

(*b*)

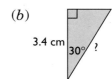

■ **6** (*a*) Choose a different set of similar right-angled triangles from the resource sheet. All these triangles will have angles of the same size.

(*b*) Choose one of the angles which is not the right angle. For each of the triangles, measure the two sides which are next to this angle.

(*c*) Make a table of results like table 1.

(*d*) Find the best value of $\frac{A}{H}$ for the whole set of triangles.

(*e*) Find the cosine of your chosen angle on your calculator.

(*f*) Compare your answers to (*d*) and (*e*).

■ **7** Find the side marked with a question mark for each of these triangles.

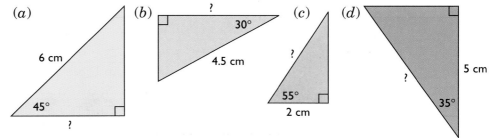

C17 page 91   F36 page 191

SINES

You could use *Spread* for the tables in this activity.

 There are five right-angled triangles on the resource sheet with an angle of 20°. The approximate lengths of two of the sides of each triangle are listed in this table. (The longest side of a right-angled triangle is called the **hypotenuse**.)

B (cm)	H (cm)	$\frac{B}{H}$
1.4	4.0	0.35
1.7	5.0	0.34
2.1	6.0	
2.4	7.0	
2.7	8.0	

Table 2

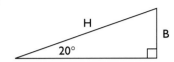

■ **1** Copy and complete the table in the box above.

 The value of $\frac{B}{H}$ is approximately the same for each triangle. If the triangles could be measured exactly you would find that the value of $\frac{B}{H}$ is exactly the same for each triangle. This value is called the **sine** of 20°, or sin 20°.

■ **2** (*a*) Decide on a best value of $\frac{B}{H}$ for the set of five triangles in table 2. Give your answer to a sensible degree of accuracy.

(*b*) Find out how to get sin 20° on your calculator. Write down sin 20° to the same degree of accuracy which you used for (*a*).

(*c*) Compare your answers to (*a*) and (*b*).

■ **3** This table describes some more right-angled triangles with an angle of 20°.

B (cm)	H (cm)	$\frac{B}{H}$ = sin 20°
5.0	14.6	0.342
	10.0	0.342
7.0		0.342
	12.8	0.342
13.45		0.342

Copy and complete this table.

 As you can see from table 2 and the table in question 3:

If you know the **hypotenuse**, to get the **side opposite to** the 20° angle you *multiply* by sin 20°.

To get the **hypotenuse** if you know the **side opposite to** the 20° angle you *divide* by sin 20°.

■ 4 (a) Choose a different set of similar right-angled triangles on the resource sheet.

(b) Choose one of the angles which is not the right angle. For each of the triangles, divide the side opposite this angle by the hypotenuse.

(c) Compare your answers to (b) with the sine of the angle.

■ 5 Find the side marked with a question mark for each of these triangles.

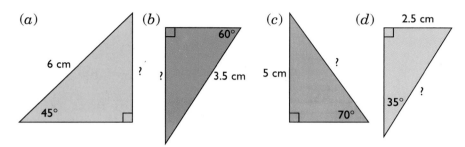

(a)   (b)   (c)   (d)

TANGENTS

You could use *Spread* for the tables in this activity.

I There are five right-angled triangles on the resource sheet with an angle of 60°. The approximate lengths of two of the sides of each triangle are listed in this table.

B (cm)	A (cm)	$\frac{B}{A}$
3.5	2.0	1.75
4.3	2.5	1.72
5.2	3.0	
6.1	3.5	
6.9	4.0	

Table 3

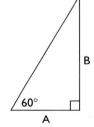

■ 1 Copy and complete the table in the box above.

I The value of $\frac{B}{A}$ is approximately the same for each triangle. If the triangles could be measured exactly you would find that the value of $\frac{B}{A}$ is exactly the same for each triangle. This value is called the **tangent** of 60°, or tan 60°.

■ 2 (a) Decide on a best value of $\frac{B}{A}$ for the set of five triangles in table 3. Give your answer to a sensible degree of accuracy.

(b) Find out how to get tan 60° on your calculator. Write down tan 60° to the same degree of accuracy which you used for (a).

(c) Compare your answers to (a) and (b).

■ **3** This table describes some more right-angled triangles with an angle of 60°.

B (cm)	A (cm)	$\frac{B}{A}$ = tan 60°
7.0	4.04	1.732
	8.0	1.732
4.5		1.732
	6.6	1.732
23.8		1.732

Copy and complete this table.

 As you can see from table 3 and the table in question 3:

If you know the **side next to** the 60° angle (not the hypotenuse), to get the **side opposite to** the 60° angle you *multiply* by tan 60°.

To get the **side next to** the 60° angle, if you know the **side opposite to** the 60° angle you *divide* by tan 60°.

■ **4** Find the side marked with a question mark for each of these triangles.

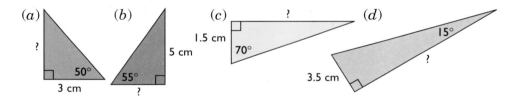

(a) ? 50° 3 cm

(b) 5 cm 55° ?

(c) ? 1.5 cm 70°

(d) 15° 3.5 cm ?

USING COSINES, SINES AND TANGENTS TO FIND LENGTHS OF SIDES

C18 page 93

1 Here are some triangles.

You need to decide whether to use the cosine, sine or tangent of the angle to find the length of the side marked with a question mark.

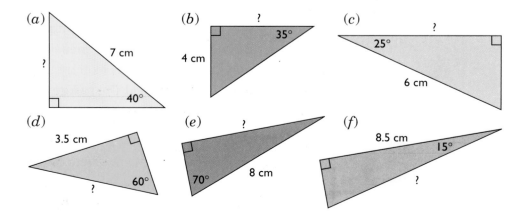

(a) 7 cm ? 40°

(b) ? 35° 4 cm

(c) 25° ? 6 cm

(d) 3.5 cm 60° ?

(e) ? 70° 8 cm

(f) 8.5 cm 15° ?

USING COSINES, SINES AND TANGENTS TO FIND ANGLES

 Look at this triangle.

Suppose you want to find the angle marked with a question mark. The two sides you know are the **hypotenuse** and another side **next to** the angle. So you use cosine. You always divide the smaller length by the larger length.

The cosine of this angle is $\frac{5}{7} = 0.7143$

To find the angle itself you can use your calculator. If you are using a scientific calculator you probably press keys in this order to find the angle.

If you are using a graphical calculator you probably press keys in this order to do the same calculation.

You should find that the angle is 44°, correct to the nearest degree.

■ **1** Find the angles marked in these triangles.

(a) 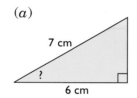 (b) 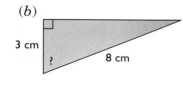 (c)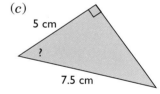

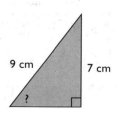 Look at this triangle.

Suppose you want to find the angle marked with a question mark. One side you know is **opposite** the angle and the other side is the **hypotenuse**. So you use sine. You always divide the smaller length by the larger length.

The sine of this angle is $\frac{7}{9} = 0.7778$

The angle is 51° correct to the nearest degree.

■ **2** Find the angles marked in these triangles. You need to use INV SIN or SHIFT SIN .

(a) 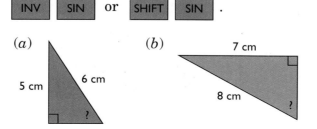 (b)   (c)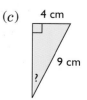

Look at this triangle.

Suppose you want to find the angle marked with a question mark.
Neither of the two sides you know is the **hypotenuse**. So you use tangent.
You always divide the side **opposite** the angle by the side **next to** it.

The tangent of this angle is $\frac{5}{3} = 1.667$

The angle is approximately 59°.

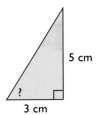

■ **3** Find the angles marked in these triangles. You need to use

INV TAN or SHIFT TAN

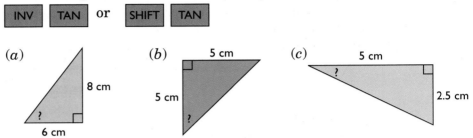

(a) 8 cm ? 6 cm

(b) 5 cm 5 cm ?

(c) 5 cm ? 2.5 cm

■ **4** Find all the angles of each of these triangles. You need to decide
whether to use INV COS , INV SIN or INV TAN

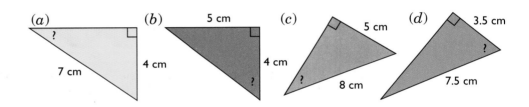

(a) ? 7 cm

(b) 5 cm 4 cm

(c) 5 cm 4 cm ? 8 cm

(d) 3.5 cm ? 7.5 cm

PROBLEMS INVOLVING TRIGONOMETRY

Here are some examples of problems which can be solved
using Pythagoras' theorem or trigonometry. To solve these
problems you have to make several assumptions. When you
have solved the problems you might want to discuss the
assumptions you have made.

■ **1** A girl is flying a kite. She estimates that the string is at an angle of
40° to the ground. The string is 25 m long. How high is the kite above
the ground?

■ **2** A ladder is 20 feet long and the angle it makes with the ground must
not be more than 65° to be safe. I want the ladder to reach a 15 foot
high gutter. Will it be safe?

■ **3** A badminton net is 5 feet high. You are standing 12 feet from the net
and hit the shuttlecock just before it reaches the ground. At what angle
must you hit the shuttlecock to clear the net?

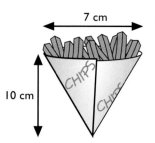

7 cm

10 cm

4 A chip cone has a diameter 7 cm and height 10 cm.

Use the blue triangle to help you work out the angle across the tip of the cone.

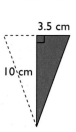

3.5 cm

10 cm

I A clinometer can be used to measure angles of elevation and angles of depression. You can use it to work out heights and distances of objects. For example, you can find the height of a tree like this.

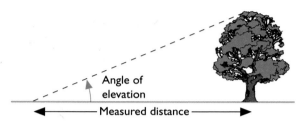

Angle of elevation

Measured distance

The distance of a ship from a lighthouse could be found like this.

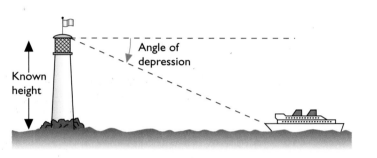

Angle of depression

Known height

5 A student measures the angle of elevation of a tree to be 20° and the tree is 35 m away. How high is the tree?

6 A lighthouse keeper in a 70 foot lighthouse sights a ship at an angle of depression of 5°. How far away is the ship?

7 A person's natural line of sight is 15° below the horizontal.

The most comfortable viewing distance for a computer screen is 550 mm.

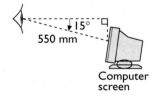

15°

550 mm

Computer screen

(a) How far away (horizontally) should a person sit from a computer screen?

(b) What height should their eyes be above the centre of the screen?

C18 page 93

8 Make up some problems involving right-angled triangles. Solve them yourself and then give them to someone else to solve.

REVIEW EXERCISES C

EXERCISE 13 Geometric Drawing

1 A piece of paper is 40 cm by 60 cm. On it two pictures are to be mounted symmetrically. Each picture is 20 cm by 30 cm.

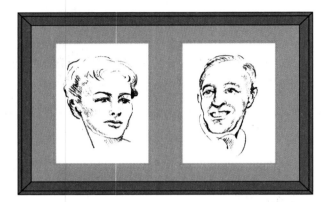

Using a scale of 1 : 5, make an accurate scale drawing of how the pictures could be arranged.

2 Draw accurately a triangle with sides of lengths 6 cm, 8 cm and 10 cm.

What are the angles of the triangle?

3 Here is sketch of a kite.

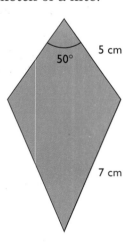

(*a*) Draw the kite accurately.

(*b*) Measure the other three angles of the kite.

4

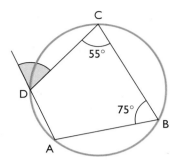

Here is a sketch of a quadrilateral drawn inside a circle.

(*a*) Draw a circle with radius 5 cm.

(*b*) Draw the line AB inside the circle so that its length is 6 cm.

(*c*) Now draw the rest of the quadrilateral accurately.

(*d*) Measure the angle marked in blue. What do you notice?

(*e*) Draw a different quadrilateral inside a circle. Measure its angles. Does the same thing happen as in (*d*)?

EXERCISE 14 Polygons and Circles

1 There are two types of quadrilaterals with two lines of symmetry.

(*a*) Draw a sketch of each type and name it.

(*b*) Mark the equal angles on each of your sketches.

2 There are two types of quadrilateral with one line of symmetry.

(*a*) Draw a sketch of each type and name it.

(*b*) Mark the equal angles on each of your sketches.

3 The cross section of a rod is a regular pentagon.

The rod is 'toppled' along a plane.

(a) Through what angle does it turn for each topple?

(b) How many topples will occur before the rod is the same way up as it started?

(c) What is the total angle through which the rod has toppled by the time this happens?

4 (a) Draw a sketch of a rhombus and its diagonals.

(b) There are twelve angles in your sketch (not counting angles which are formed of two or more angles).

Show which of these twelve angles are equal.

(c) If one of the angles of the original rhombus is 40°, find the sizes of the twelve angles.

5 (a) Draw a sketch of a regular pentagon with all its diagonals.

(b) There are 35 angles in your sketch.

Show which of the 35 angles are equal.

(c) Find the sizes of the 35 angles.

6 An equilateral triangle ABC is drawn inside a circle. M is the midpoint of BC. The line AM is continued until it meets the circle at D.

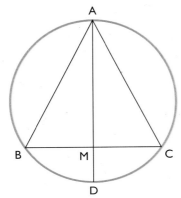

(a) What can you say about the line AD?

(b) What are the three angles of the triangle BDC?

7 Draw a sketch of a kite inside a circle.

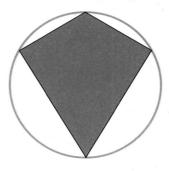

Mark in the line of symmetry.

If one angle of the kite is 50° find the other three angles.

8 Here is a circle together with a radius and a tangent.

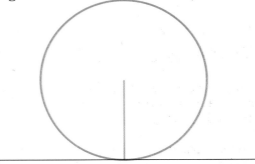

(a) What type of symmetry does this drawing have?

(b) What does this tell you about the angle between the radius and the tangent?

9 (a) AB is the diameter of a circle and AT is a tangent. The angle CAT is $x°$.

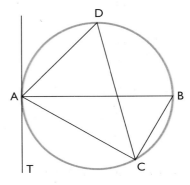

Find in terms of x, the following angles:

(i) BAC (ii) ABC (iii) ADC

(b) What is the size of the blue angle in this picture?

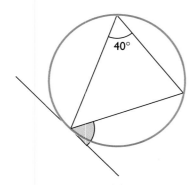

EXERCISE 15 Loci

1 Draw two points A and B which are 8 cm apart. Draw the path of a point P which moves so that the distances PA and PB are always the same.

2 Draw two lines CD and CE with an angle of 70° between them.

Draw the path of a point P which moves so that its distance from the line CD is always equal to its distance from the line CE.

3 Draw several circles all with radius 5 cm through a point H. On what do the centres of all these circles lie?

4 Draw two points F and G, 6 cm apart.

(a) Draw several circles which pass through F and G.

(b) On what do the centres of all these circles lie?

■ 5 (a) Draw accurately a triangle XYZ. XY is 5 cm, YZ is 7 cm and XZ is 9 cm.

(b) Draw accurately the locus of the centres of circles which pass through X and Y.

(c) Draw accurately the locus of the centres of circles which pass through Y and Z.

(d) What circle can be drawn with its centre at the point where these two loci meet?

■ 6 Two points U and V are 10 cm apart. Two adjacent sides of a square pass through the points U and V.

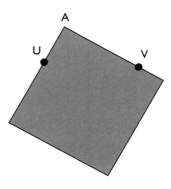

What is the locus of the corner of the square labelled A?

■ 7 Two points J and K are 12 cm apart.

Two sides of an equilateral triangle pass through the points J and K.

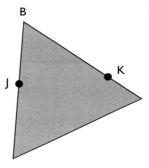

What is the locus of the vertex of the triangle labelled B?

■ 8 Describe fully the locus of each of the eight vertices of a cube:

(a) if it moves so that one of its edges is fixed.

(b) if it moves so that one of its vertices is fixed.

(c) if it moves so that one of its face diagonals is fixed.

(d) if it moves so that one of its main diagonals is fixed.

EXERCISE 16 Without a Calculator

1 (*a*) Sidhartha buys a can of Coke for 35p and a packet of crisps for 22p.

What is his change from a £5 note?

(*b*) Emily buys three cans of Coke and five packets of crisps. What is her change from a £10 note?

2

> # SPECIAL OFFER
>
> *Settees £357.85 each*
>
> *Chairs £227.85 each*

Find the total cost of a settee and two chairs.

3 Find the following:

(*a*) 40×20

(*b*) 50×200

(*c*) 800×700

(*d*) $600 \div 30$

(*e*) $1500 \div 500$

(*f*) $24\,000 \div 80$

4 Find the following:

(*a*) 37×14

(*b*) 38×14

(*c*) 380×14

(*d*) 381×14

5 Find the following:

(*a*) 529×35

(*b*) 529×36

(*c*) 529×360

(*d*) 529×720

6 Find the following:

(*a*) $1462 \div 43$

(*b*) $14\,620 \div 43$

(*c*) $14\,663 \div 43$

7 Find the following:

(*a*) $35 \times 26 - 36 \times 25$

(*b*) $47 \times 38 - 48 \times 37$

(*c*) $470 \times 380 - 480 \times 370$

(*d*) $23 \times 19 - 25 \times 17$

(*e*) $35 \times 26 - 38 \times 23$

8 (*a*) The temperature falls from 10°C to −8°C. How much of a fall is that?

(*b*) It then rises to −3°C. By how much does it rise?

(*c*) It then drops by 10°. What temperature is it now?

(*d*) It then rises by 15°. What temperature is it now?

EXERCISE 17 Ratio and Similarity

1

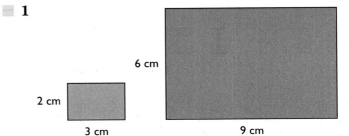

(*a*) Explain why these two rectangles are similar.

(*b*) What is the ratio of their perimeters?

(*c*) What is the ratio of their areas?

2 A red ball and a blue ball start at opposite ends of a track 1 metre long. They move towards each other.

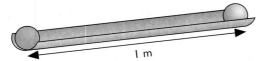

(a) Where do the balls meet if the red ball travels twice as fast as the blue ball?

(b) Where do they meet if the red ball travels three times as fast as the blue ball?

(c) Where do they meet if the ratio of the speed of the red ball to the speed of the blue ball is 3:4?

3 These two triangles are similar.

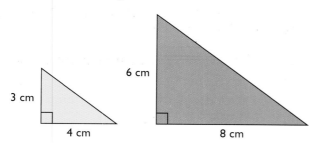

(a) Find the perimeters of the triangles.

(b) What is the ratio of the perimeters of the triangles?

(c) What is the ratio of the areas of the triangles?

4

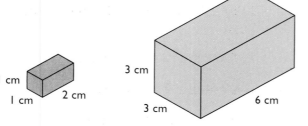

(a) Explain why these two cuboids are similar.

(b) What is the ratio of their surface areas?

(c) What is the ratio of their volumes?

5 In this question give the scale of each plan in the form 1:k.

(a) The plan of a classroom is drawn with 2 cm representing 1 metre.

What is the scale of the plan?

(b) The plan of a school's ground is drawn with 1 inch representing 50 yards.

What is the scale of the plan?

[There are 12 inches in a foot and 3 feet in a yard.]

(c) A map of the area round the school is drawn with 4 cm representing 1 kilometre.

What is the scale of the map?

6 (a)

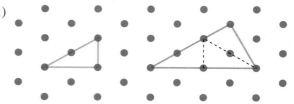

(i) What is the ratio of the areas of these two triangles?

(ii) What is the ratio of the perimeters of these two triangles?

(b)

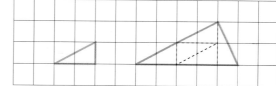

(i) What is the ratio of the areas of these two triangles?

(ii) What is the ratio of the perimeters of these two triangles?

7

The capacities of these three olive oil bottles are 250 ml, 500 ml and 1 litre.

(a) What is the ratio of their volumes?

(b) The middle-sized bottle holds 460 g of olive oil. How much do the other bottles hold?

(c) The ratio of unsaturated to saturated fat in the oil is about 11:2. What weight of saturated fat is there in the large bottle?

(d) The height of the biggest bottle is 23 cm. Assuming that the three bottles are all the same shape find the approximate heights of the other two bottles.

EXERCISE 18   Trigonometry

■ **1** Find the missing sides of these triangles.

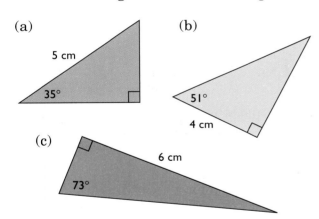

(a)

(b)

(c)

■ **2** Find the angles of these triangles.

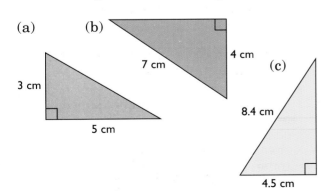

(a)

(b)

(c)

■ **3** A woman walks 6 miles East and then 8 miles South.

(a) How far is she from her starting point?

(b) On what bearing should she walk to return to her starting point by the shortest route?

■ **4** When I stand 50 yards from a church the angle of elevation of the top of the church spire is 22°. Find the height of the church spire in feet.

[1 yard is 3 feet.]

■ **5** One of the angles of an isosceles triangle is 70°. Two of the sides of the triangle are 10 cm long.

Find the length of the other side. (There are two possible answers.)

■ **6** The sides of a regular pentagon are 10 cm long.

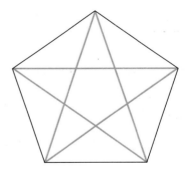

■ **7** Find the lengths of the diagonals of the pentagon.

(a) Draw a graph of $y = \sin x°$.

(b) Draw a graph of $y = \cos x°$.

(c) Draw a graph of $y = \tan x°$.

(d) Two of the graphs are the same shape. Which two? What transformation would change one of them into the other?

10 IS IT TRUE?

Cassettes are more popular than CDs.

Teenagers buy singles. Adults buy albums.

Teenagers listen to music more than any other age group.

Teenagers watch TV more than they listen to music.

Boys spend more on tapes and records than girls.

Hardly any teenagers listen to classical music.

People listen to most of their music on cassettes.

People either listen to pop music or classical music but not both.

This task is about how you can find out whether statements like these are true. You can make use of the statistical techniques and methods of displaying data which you might already have met in this book or in books 1 and 2.

ASKING THE RIGHT QUESTIONS

1 This is a question from a student's questionnaire asking about people's musical tastes.

> What kind of music do you like?

(*a*) How would you answer this question?

(*b*) Ask some other people what their answer would be. Write a list of all the possible answers you can think of.

(*c*) Do you think this is a good question for a questionnaire? If not, how would you improve it?

2 Here is another version of the same question, produced on a database.

What kind of music do you like?
- ❏ chart music
- ❏ rave
- ❏ indie
- ❏ rap/reggae
- ❏ heavy metal

(*a*) How would you answer this question?

(*b*) Is this a good question for a questionnaire? If not, how would you improve it?

3 This question was given out to a class to answer. Here are their replies.

Do you know how many people answered the question?

Type of music	Number of people
chart music	8
rave	6
indie	3
rap/reggae	4
heavy metal	4

4 The purpose of each of the following questions is to find out whether people think the quality of sound you get from CDs is better than that from cassette tapes.

A.
> *Do you think that CDs are better than cassettes?*

B.
> CDs have a better sound than cassettes.
> ❏ agree
> ❏ disagree

C.
> *Do you agree that CDs have a better sound quality than cassettes?*

D.
> Which of the following do you think gives the better sound?
> ❏ CDs
> ❏ cassettes
> ❏ no difference
> ❏ don't know

E.
> *Tick the statement you agree with:*
> ❏ *CDs have a better sound than cassettes*
> ❏ *cassettes have a better sound than CDs*
> ❏ *there is not much difference in sound between CDs and cassettes*

Say what are the good and bad features of each of the questions.

5 The purpose of this question is to find out how much people spend on cassettes, CDs and records.

> How much do you spend on cassettes, CDs and records?

(*a*) What would your answer to this question be?

(*b*) Rewrite the question so it would be easier to analyse all the answers when the questionnaires were returned.

> *14-year-olds spend 35% of their pocket money on cassettes, records and CDs.*

6 (*a*) Make a list of the facts you would need to find out if you want to test whether or not this statement is true.

(*b*) Write down the questions you could use to discover these facts.

> *Teenagers listen to music more than any other age group.*

7 (*a*) Make a list of the facts you would need to find out if you want to test whether or not this statement is true.

(*b*) Write down the questions you could use to discover these facts.

WHOM DO YOU ASK?

 The set of people who are asked to complete a questionnaire is called **a sample.**

1   A student wants to find out whether girls or boys spent more on cassettes, CDs and records. She has 50 questionnaires to give out. Whom should she give them to?

2   A student wants to find out what is the most popular type of music amongst teenagers. He gives out his questionnaire one evening to people attending a youth club where a local up-and-coming group are playing a gig.

   Is this a good way of choosing a sample?

3   A student wants to find out if this statement is true.

   (a) What sort of people should she ask?

   (b) How many people should she ask?

   (c) Where would she find suitable people to ask?

> 14-year-olds spend 35% of their pocket money on cassettes, records and CDs.

> Teenagers listen to music more than any other age group.

4   A student wants to find out if this statement is true.

   (a) What sort of people should he ask?

   (b) How many people should he ask?

   (c) Where would he find suitable people to ask?

SORTING OUT YOUR DATA

 If a questionnaire has been designed carefully then it is much easier to sort out the data and analyse the results.

If a computer database, such as *Pinpoint* has been used then it will do most of the work.

Tally charts are helpful. Working with another person makes it easier to tally. One person reads out the answers while the other tallies.

You have to decide what to do about people who have not answered all the questions, or who have given an answer you did not expect.

Check all your figures by adding up the totals. The following questions show how this can be done.

1 A group of four students gave out 100 questionnaire, and 76 of them were returned. They drew up this table to show who replied, classified by gender and by age.

Age	Girls	Boys	Total
13 years	4	5	
14 years	25	20	
15 years	10	11	
Total			

(a) How many males replied to the questionnaire?

(b) How many 14-year-olds replied to the questionnaire?

(c) The students suddenly realised that they had made a mistake in producing their table. How did they know?

2 Another group of students was finding out whether people in their class bought more music on records or on cassettes. Here is one of their tables of results.

This isn't right. There are only 27 of us in the class.

	Number
People who bought records	21
People who bought cassettes	9
People who bought neither	5

It is ! I've double-checked all the questionnaires.

Can you explain their results?

3 A third group of students was trying to find out whether girls listened to more music than boys. Here is their table of results.

Number of hours listening during last week	Girls	Boys	Total
Less than 5	1	2	
5 to 9	7	5	
10 to 14	11	8	
15 to 19	15	7	
20 or more	4	7	
Total			

(a) They had 67 questionnaires returned. Do the totals in their table agree with this fact?

(b) One of the students knew that 39 girls had returned the questionnaire, and so she realised they must have made a mistake. Another student knew that only one boy listened to music less than 5 hours a week.

Can you correct the table for them?

DISPLAYING YOUR DATA

On this page there are examples of many different ways of displaying data. Discuss with other people the advantages and disadvantages of each type of display method. What sort of data would you use each display method for?

Pictogram

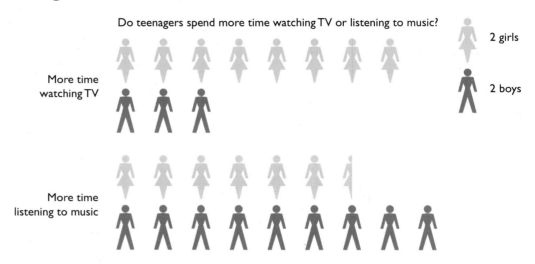

Do teenagers spend more time watching TV or listening to music?

2 girls

2 boys

More time watching TV

More time listening to music

Line graph

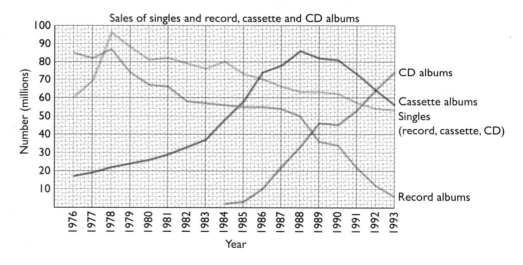

Sales of singles and record, cassette and CD albums

Number (millions)

CD albums

Cassette albums

Singles (record, cassette, CD)

Record albums

Year

Pie chart

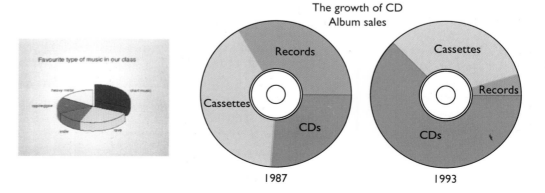

Favourite type of music in our class

The growth of CD Album sales

Records

Cassettes

CDs

1987

Cassettes

Records

CDs

1993

This pie chart was drawn using *Pinpoint*

Strip chart

These are like pie charts, but are sometimes better when you want to compare one thing with another.

Private copying
Ownership of CDs, cassettes and records

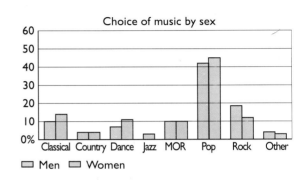

This 3-dimensional bar chart was drawn using *Pinpoint*

Bar chart

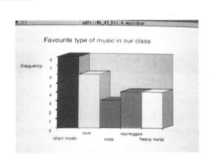

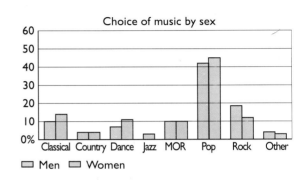

Frequency polygon

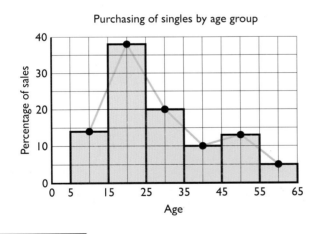

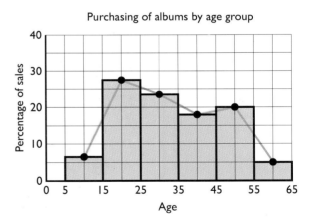

If you draw your own pie charts you could use the resource sheet *Percentage pie charts*.

If your figures are not percentages you have to calculate the size of the angle to use for each slice of pie.

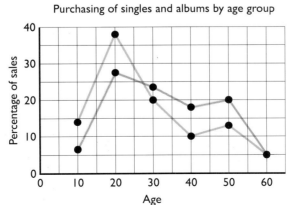

Purchasing of singles and albums by age group

—— Albums —— Singles

Frequency polygons help you to compare two bar charts.

You could also use *scatter graphs* and *cumulative frequency curves*. They are explained in task 5 on pages 44 and 46.

D19
page
124

ANALYSING YOUR DATA

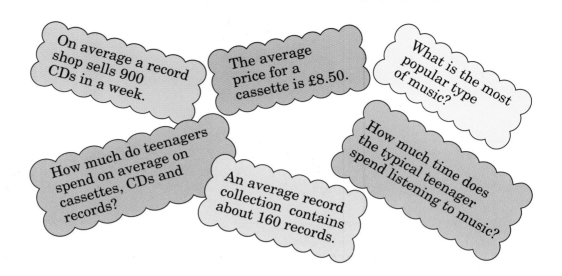

On average a record shop sells 900 CDs in a week.

The average price for a cassette is £8.50.

What is the most popular type of music?

How much do teenagers spend on average on cassettes, CDs and records?

An average record collection contains about 160 records.

How much time does the typical teenager spend listening to music?

All the bubbles above are about finding the most representative piece of data – the 'average'.

Mean, **median** and **mode** are different types of average.

---

1 Discuss with some other people how you find

(*a*) the mode

(*b*) the median

(*c*) the mean

of a set of data.

2 Look at the bubbles above.

Say whether you would choose the mode, the median or the mean for each bubble.

Some boys are fanatical about listening to records and others are always playing sport and never listen to anything. But girls are more sensible and middle of the road.

One way of investigating whether statements like this are true is to use the **range**, the difference between the biggest and smallest pieces of data. Alternatively, you can use the **interquartile range**. This is explained on page 47.

People who go to lots of pop concerts also buy lots of records and tapes.

D19
page
124

I One way of investigating whether statements like this are true is to use a **scatter graph**. Sometimes a **line of best fit** is helpful. These are explained on page 44.

IS IT TRUE?

D20
page
125

Think up a statement of your own. It does not have to be about music. Find out whether or not it is true.

- Design a questionnaire
- Select your sample
- Organise the data you collect
- Display your data
- Analyse your data
- Draw conclusions.

You could use a computer database such as *Pinpoint*.

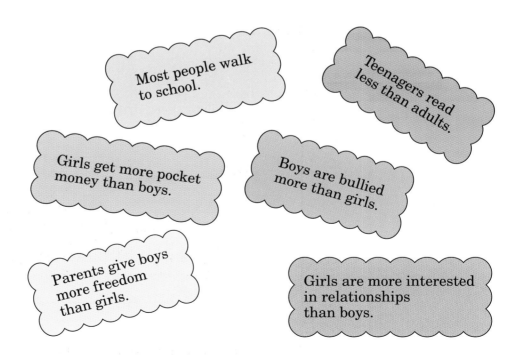

Most people walk to school.

Teenagers read less than adults.

Girls get more pocket money than boys.

Boys are bullied more than girls.

Parents give boys more freedom than girls.

Girls are more interested in relationships than boys.

ARITHMAGONS

ADDING

All the numbers used in this activity are positive whole numbers.

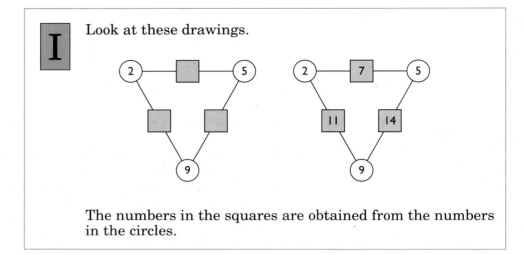

Look at these drawings.

The numbers in the squares are obtained from the numbers in the circles.

1 Copy and complete these drawings. Use the rule in the box above.

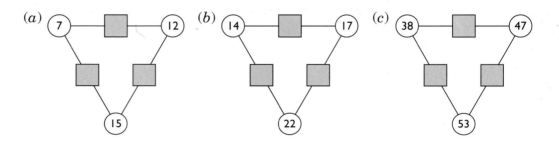

2 Copy and complete these drawings.

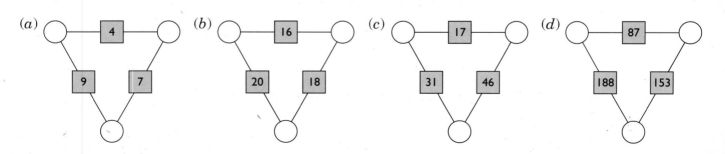

3 Make up some problems of your own by putting numbers in circles, as in question 1. (Only use positive whole numbers in the circles.) Work out the numbers in the squares.

4 Give other people the numbers you put into the *squares* for question 3.

See if they can find the numbers you used in the circles.

A trio of numbers in the squares obtained by starting with positive whole numbers in the circles could be called an *adding* trio.

Here are the adding trios in questions 1 and 2:

22, 19, 27	4, 7, 9
31, 39, 36	16, 18, 20
85, 100, 91	17, 31, 46
	87, 153, 188

You might want to discuss your ideas for 5(b) with other people.

5 (a) What adding trios did you produce for question 3?

(b) What is special about the three numbers in an adding trio?

(c) Which of these trios of numbers are adding trios? If you are not sure you could try using them in the squares of an arithmagon.

6, 7, 11	12, 15, 19
4, 8, 9	22, 34, 58
3, 6, 7	55, 66, 77
3, 5, 10	

6 In this arithmagon x, y, and z are whole numbers.

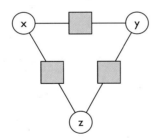

(a) Copy and complete the arithmagon.

(b) What is the sum of the numbers in the squares?

(c) What sort of number is the answer to (b)?

7 Copy and complete these drawings.

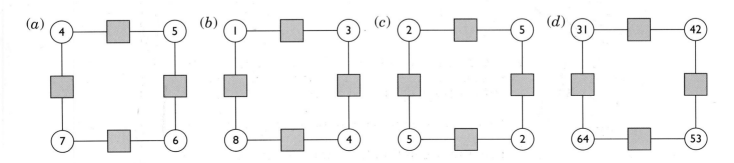

8 Copy and complete these drawings. How many different ways are there of completing each drawing?

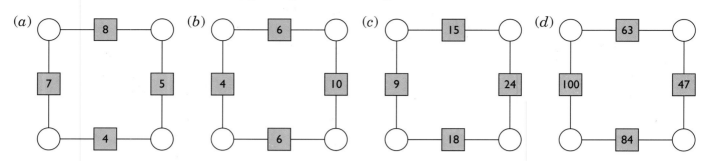

(a) 8, 7, 5, 4

(b) 6, 4, 10, 6

(c) 15, 9, 24, 18

(d) 63, 100, 47, 84

9 Make up some problems of your own by putting numbers in circles, as in question 7. (Only use positive whole numbers in the circles.) Work out the numbers in the squares.

10 Give other people the numbers you put into the *squares* for question 9.

See if they can find the numbers you used in the circles.

11 Here are the adding quartets of numbers in questions 7 and 8:

9, 11, 13, 11   8, 5, 4, 7
4, 7, 12, 9   15, 24, 18, 9
7, 7, 7, 7   63, 47, 84, 100
73, 95, 117, 95

(a) What adding quartets did you produce for question 9?

(b) What is special about the four numbers in an adding quartet?

(c) Which of these are adding quartets?

4, 6, 8, 10
4, 6, 10, 8
5, 5, 5, 5
12, 13, 8, 17
8, 21, 34, 13

12 Use algebra to explain your answers to question 11.

13 Find some adding quintets and adding sextets.

Give them to other people to find out which circle numbers produced them. When is there more than one answer?

Make up some quintets and sextets of numbers and explain whether or not they are adding quintets or sextets.

Use algebra to explain some of your results.

C16
page
91

MULTIPLYING

All the numbers used in this activity are positive whole numbers.

 Look at these drawings.

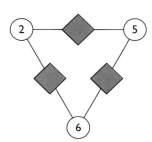 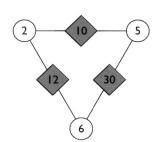

The numbers in the diamonds are obtained from the numbers in the circles.

1 Copy and complete these drawings. Use the rule in the box above.

(a) 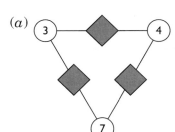   (b) 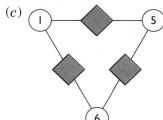   (c) 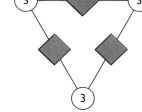   (d)

2 Copy and complete these drawings.

(a) 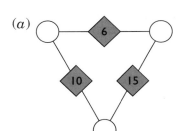   (b) 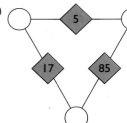   (c) 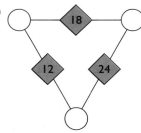   (d)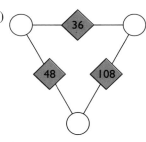

3 Find all the ways of completing each of these drawings. (Remember that the numbers in the circles must all be positive whole numbers.) How many answers are possible for each drawing?

(a) 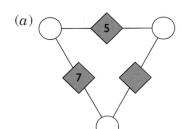   (b) 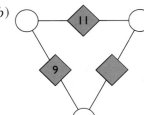   (c) 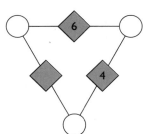   (d)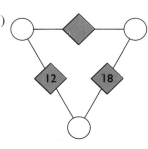

4 Make up some drawings of your own where two of the diamonds are filled in. Try to find drawings with 1 answer, 2 answers, 3 answers, 4 answers, . . .

5 How many ways are there of completing this drawing? What numbers are possible for the third diamond?

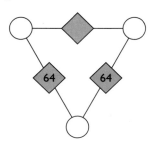

6 Make up a drawing like question 5 where the numbers 1, 4, 9, 16 and 25 are all possible numbers for the third diamond.

7 Make up some drawings of your own by putting three numbers in circles, as in question 1. (Only use positive whole numbers in the circles.) Work out the numbers in the diamonds.

8 Give other people the numbers you put into the *diamonds* for question 7.

See if they can find the numbers you used in the circles.

 I A trio of numbers in the diamonds obtained by starting with positive whole numbers in the circles could be called a *multiplying* trio.

Here are the multiplying trios in questions 1 and 2:

12, 28, 21	6, 10, 15
8, 36, 18	5, 17, 85
5, 30, 6	18, 24, 12
9, 9, 9	36, 108, 48

9 (*a*) What multiplying trios did you produce for question 7?

(*b*) What is special about the three numbers in a multiplying trio?

(*c*) Which of these trios of numbers are multiplying trios?

4, 4, 4	2, 36, 72
6, 6, 6	3, 3, 16
4, 5, 20	24, 50, 300
12, 15, 20	3, 8, 96

C16
page
91

USING OTHER NUMBERS

1 These trios of numbers are not adding trios. However, they can be produced in the squares of an arithmagon if you use negative numbers and fractions or decimals.

7, 4, 8
2, 6, 12
14, 17, 53
18, 19, 20

> For this activity the numbers used are not all positive whole numbers.

The diagram shows how the first trio can be produced.

Find the numbers in the circles to produce each of the other trios.

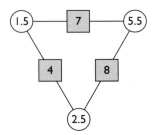

2 Copy and complete these drawings.

(a) 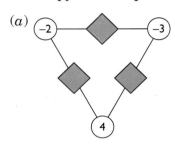 (b) 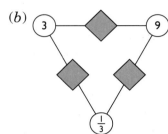 (c)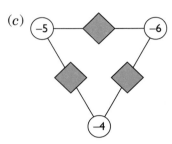

3 Find all the ways of completing each of these drawings. (Don't forget that negative numbers can be used.)

(a) 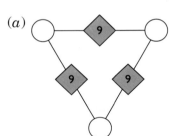 (b) 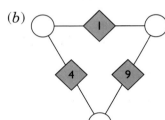 (c) 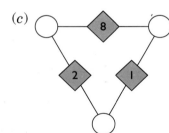 (d)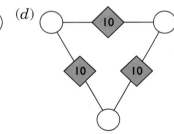

4 Copy and complete these arithmagons.

(a) 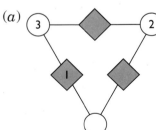 (b) 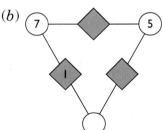 (c)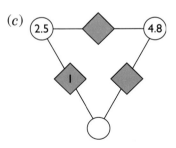

5 Make up some more arithmagons where you start by filling two circles and a diamond.

Solve them. Then give them to someone else to solve.

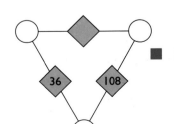

6 (a) How many ways are there of completing this drawing using whole numbers?

(b) By using numbers other than whole numbers find a way of getting 6 in the third diamond.

(c) Find a way of getting 7 in the third diamond.

■ **7** Copy and complete these drawings.

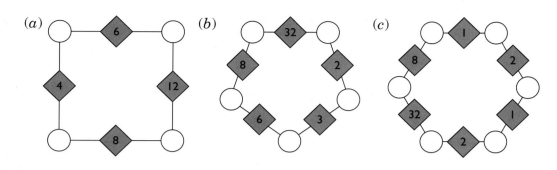

(a)   (b)   (c)

E25
page
152

C16
page
91

■ **8** Make up questions of your own and answer them.

SQUARES AND DIAMONDS

I Here is a drawing containing squares and diamonds.

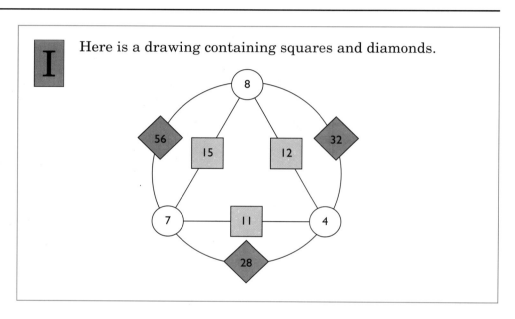

■ **1** Copy and complete these drawings.

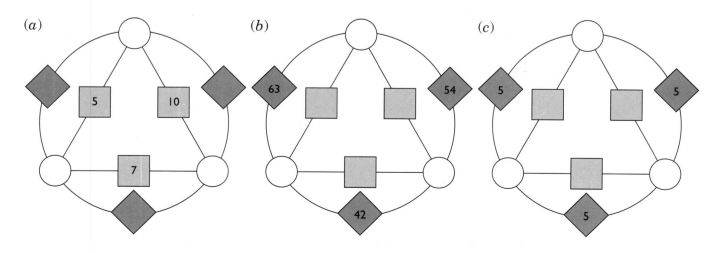

(a)   (b)   (c)

For question 2 you might want to use algebra. You could use *x*, *y* and *z* in the three circles; or just *x* in one of the circles.

2 Copy and complete these drawings.

(a)
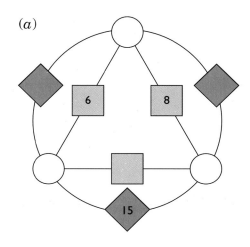

(b)
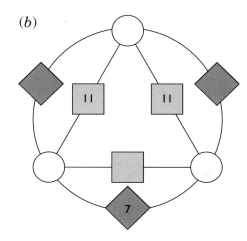

(c)
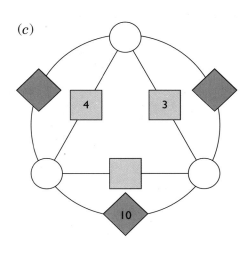

(d)
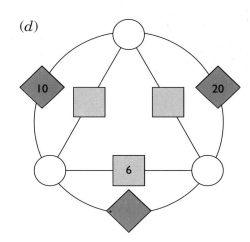

(e)
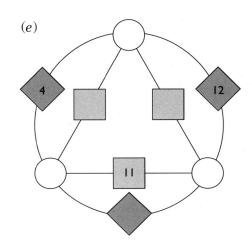

(f)
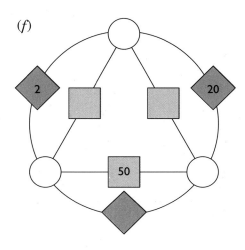

B12 page 63

3 Make up some more drawings like the ones in question 2 and work out the answers. Then give them to someone else to work out.

TETRAHEDRA

I The numbers at the corners of this tetrahedron are 3, 4, 5 and 7.

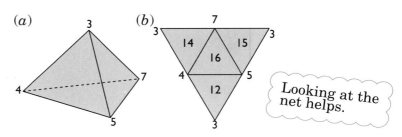

(a)

(b)

Looking at the net helps.

The numbers on the faces are 12, 14, 15 and 16. The number on one face is 12 because this is the sum of the three numbers at its corners (3 + 4 + 5).

1 Find the numbers on the faces for each of these tetrahedra.

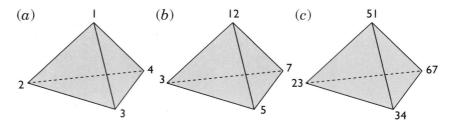

(a)

(b)

(c)

2 Find the numbers at the corners for each of these tetrahedra.

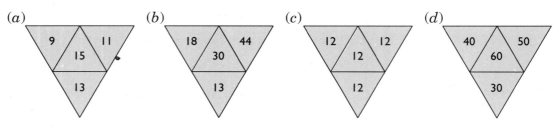

(a)

(b)

(c)

(d)

3 What about these tetrahedra?

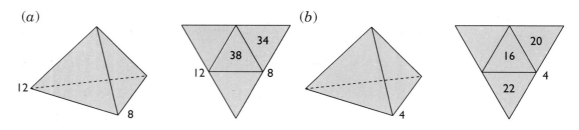

(a)

(b)

4 Start with positive whole numbers on the faces.

(a) Do you always get whole numbers at the corners? If not, when do you get whole numbers?

(b) Do you always get positive numbers at the corners? If not, when do you get positive numbers?

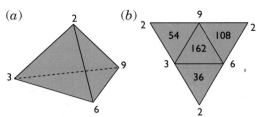

> **I** The numbers at the corners of this tetrahedron are 2, 3, 6 and 9.
>
> *(a)*   *(b)*
>
> The numbers on the faces are 36, 54, 108 and 162. The number on one face is 108 because this is the product of the three numbers at its corners ($2 \times 6 \times 9$).

5   Find the numbers on the faces for each of these tetrahedra.

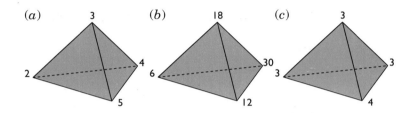

(a)   *(b)*   *(c)*

6   Which of the following are possible for red tetrahedra?

    (a) Square numbers on no faces

    (b) Square numbers on one face

    (c) Square numbers on two faces

    (d) Square numbers on three faces

    (e) Square numbers on four faces

F36 page 191

> You could try to get prime numbers on the faces.
> Or cube numbers.
> Or. . . .

7   *(a)* Can you get the number 27 on each of the faces of a red tetrahedron?

    (b) Can you get the number 10 on each of the faces of a red tetrahedron?

8   Can you get a red tetrahedron with the number 1 on two of its faces?

9   Make up other questions about tetrahedra and answer them.

10   Use other solid shapes instead of tetrahedra.

    Answer the same kinds of questions. Or make up questions of your own.

> You could try to get the same numbers on the faces of a red tetrahedron as on the faces of a blue tetrahedron

 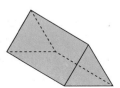

12 SEEING THE CONNECTION

COORDINATES

1 Here are some pairs of coordinates:

(1, 4), (5, 8), (30, 33), (45, 48)

(a) Can you see the connection? Write down some more pairs of coordinates that fit the pattern.

(b) Copy these axes onto squared paper.

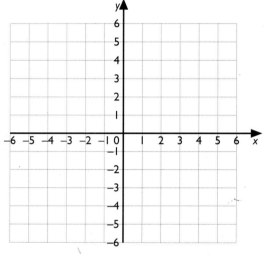

(c) Some of your answers to part (a) can be plotted on the axes. Plot them.

(d) Some of your answers to part (a) cannot be plotted on the axes. Why is this?

(e) Can you see a connection between the points you have plotted on the axes? Would drawing a line help you to explain the connection?

(f) Did you use negative numbers when you answered part (a)? If not, write down some more pairs of coordinates that fit the pattern, using negative numbers.

(g) Did you use fractions or decimals when answering part (a)? If not, write down some more pairs of coordinates that fit the pattern, using fractions or decimals.

2 Here are some pairs of coordinates:

(3, 5), (6, 8), (−4, −2), (35, 37), (999, 1001)

Answer question 1 for these pairs of coordinates.

3 Compare the picture for the first set of coordinates with the picture for the second. How are they the same? How are they different?

4 What would the picture for these coordinates look like?

(3, 7), (5, 9), (14, 18), . . .

The coordinates in question 1 obey a simple rule:

The second coordinate is 3 more than the first.

This rule (or equation) is usually written (using algebra) like this:

$y = x + 3$

5 (*a*) Write down (using algebra) the equation for the coordinates in question 2.

(*b*) Write down the equation for the coordinates in question 4.

 The picture for the coordinates in question 1 looks like this:

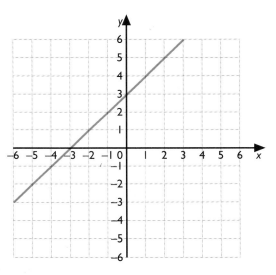

The picture is said to be the **graph** of $y = x + 3$.

Suppose you want to draw the graph of $y = x + 5$. One way to do this is to find some coordinates which satisfy the rule. Then you can plot these coordinates and draw a line.

6 (*a*) Draw the graph of $y = x + 5$.

(*b*) Using the same axes, draw the graph of $y = x + 1$.

(*c*) Draw the graph of $y = x + 4$.

(*d*) By now you might be seeing a pattern. If so, draw the graph of $y = x + 6$ *without* finding any coordinates which fit the rule.

(*e*) Draw the graph of $y = x - 2$.

(*f*) Draw the graph of $y = x$.

7 (*a*) Make up some more coordinates that obey the same rule as these:

$(3, 5), (7, 1), (2, 6)$

(*b*) Write down the equation for these coordinates.

(*c*) Draw the graph for this equation.

8 On the same axes that you used for question 7, draw graphs of the following:

(*a*) $x + y = 7$

(*b*) $x + y = 5$

(*c*) $x + y = 4$

9 (*a*) Make up some more coordinates that obey the same rule as these:

$(3, 6), (7, 14), (1, 2)$

(*b*) Write down the equation for these coordinates.

(*c*) Draw the graph for this equation.

10 On the same axes which you used for question 9, draw the following graphs:

(*a*) $y = 2x + 2$

(*b*) $y = 2x - 3$

(*c*) $y = 2x + 3$

11 Draw the graph of $y = 3x$.

12 On the same axes which you used for question 11 draw the following graphs:

(*a*) $y = 2x$

(*b*) $y = x$

(*c*) $y = -2x$

D21
page
125

The sign $\leq$ means 'less than or equal to'.

For example:

$5 \leq 8$

$3 \leq 4$

$2 \leq 20$

$6 \leq 6$

Here is one way in which this sign can be used. *All* the following coordinates satisfy the rule $y \leq x$

$(8, 5), (4, 3), (20, 2), (6, 6)$

The symbol $\geq$ means 'greater than or equal to'.

■ **13** Look at these coordinates:

(1, 3), (2, 4), (3, 0), (0, 5)

These coordinates obey all three of these rules:

$x + y \leq 6$

$x \geq 0$

$y \geq 0$

(a) Make up some more coordinates which obey all these three rules.

(b) Draw some axes. Plot all your coordinates.

(c) Draw the triangle inside which *all* the coordinates must lie.

■ **14** Some coordinates obey these three rules:

$x \geq 0$

$y \leq 4$

$y \geq x$

(a) Make up some coordinates which obey these rules.

(b) Plot these coordinates on some axes.

(c) Draw the triangle inside which all these coordinates must lie.

■ **15** Some coordinates obey these three rules:

$y \geq 0$

$x \leq 6$

$y \leq 2x$

(a) Make up some coordinates which obey these rules.

(b) Plot these coordinates on some axes.

(c) Draw the triangle inside which all these coordinates must lie.

D22
page
127

■ **16** This diagram is similar to those you produced for questions 13, 14 and 15.

What are the four rules which all the coordinates in the shaded shape must satisfy?

$y = mx + c$

You might find it helpful to use a graphical calculator or a computer graph plotter for question 1. You might also find it helpful to work in a group with other people.

I In the previous activity you looked at graphs of equations like these:

$$y = x + 4$$
$$y = 2x + 3$$
$$y = x - 2$$

All these equations have the same pattern

$$y = mx + c$$

m and c stand for numbers.

All these equations have similar types of graph. They are all straight lines.

The values of m and c tell us where the line is to be drawn.

1 Write down some equations by choosing different values for m and c.

Produce graphs for the equations you have written down.

What does c tell you about where the straight line is?

What does m tell you about where the straight line is?

The value of m gives the gradient of the straight line. The idea of a gradient is explained in more detail in review exercise D21 on page 125.

2 What are the equations of the lines in these two diagrams?

(a)

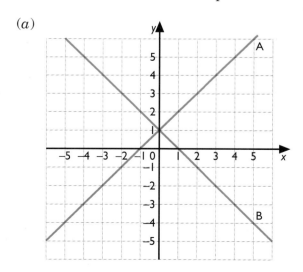

(b)

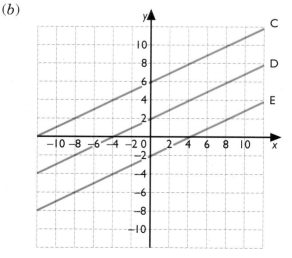

You could use a graphical calculator or a graph plotter to produce the patterns in question 2.

■ **3** Each of these patterns is produced using graphs of the form $y = mx + c$.

Suggest possible equations for the lines in each graph. (There is more than one answer.)

(a)

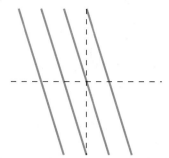

(b)

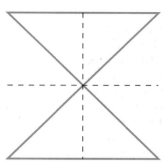

(c)

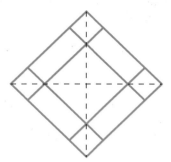

(d)

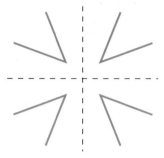

■ **4** Each of these patterns is produced by shading points according to a set of rules.

Suggest possible rules for producing each pattern.

(You need to use the signs $\leq$ and $\geq$ in your rules.)

(a)

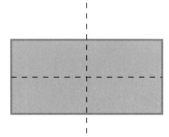

(b)

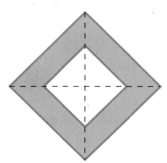

(c)

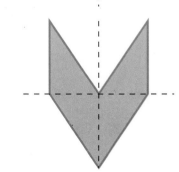

(d)

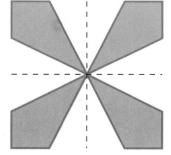

D21 page 125

D22 page 127

QUADRATICS AND OTHER GRAPHS

1 Here are some pairs of coordinates:

(1, 1), (3, 9), (5, 25), (20, 400), (−4, 16)

(a) Can you see the connection? Write down some more pairs of coordinates that fit the pattern. Use negative numbers for some pairs.

(b) Copy these axes onto squared paper.

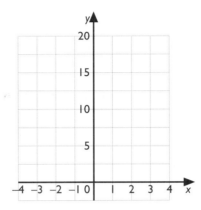

(c) Some of your answers to question (a) can be plotted on the axes. Plot these.

(d) Draw a smooth curve through the points you have plotted on the axes. What is the equation of this curve?

> You might find it helpful to use a graphical calculator or a computer graph plotter for questions 2 to 8. You might also find it helpful to work in a group with other people.

2 (a) Produce graphs for these three equations on the same axes:

$y = x^2 + 1$ $y = x^2 + 5$ $y = x^2 - 4$

(b) What is the same about these three graphs? What is different?

3 (a) Produce graphs for these four equations on the same axes:

$y = x^2$ $y = 3x^2$ $y = 2x^2$ $y = -2x^2$

(b) What is the same about these four graphs? What is different?

4 Produce some pairs of coordinates for the rule $y = x^2 + 2x - 5$.

Plot these coordinates on some axes.

Join them up with a smooth curve.

Check your graph by using a graph plotter.

5 (a) Produce graphs for these four equations on the same axes:

$y = x^2$ $y = x^2 + 4x$ $y = x^2 + 2x$ $y = x^2 - 4x$

(b) What is the same about these four graphs? What is different?

■ **6** (*a*) Produce graphs for these four equations on the same axes:

$y = x$ $y = x^3$

$y = x^2$ $y = x^4$

(*b*) What is the same about these four graphs? What is different?

■ **7** Here are some pairs of coordinates:

$(1, 24), (2, 12), (6, 4), (12, 2)$

(*a*) Can you see the connection? Write down some more pairs of coordinates that fit the pattern. Use negative numbers for some pairs.

(*b*) Copy these axes onto graph paper.

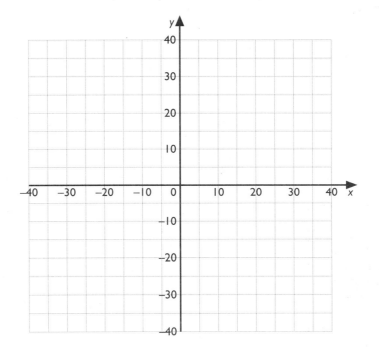

(*c*) Some of your answers to question (*a*) can be plotted on the axes. Plot them.

(*d*) Join up the points you have plotted with a smooth curve, but think carefully first. (To get this right it might be helpful to choose some very small numbers for some of your coordinates.)

(*e*) What is the equation of the curve?

■ **8** (*a*) Produce graphs for these two equations on the same axes you used for question 7.

$y = \dfrac{36}{x}$ $y = \dfrac{18}{x}$

(*b*) What is the same about these three graphs? What is different?

DIRECT AND INVERSE PROPORTION

1 It costs £2 for one person to get into an amusement park.

(a) How much does it cost 3 people?

(b) How much does it cost 10 people?

(c) Copy these axes.

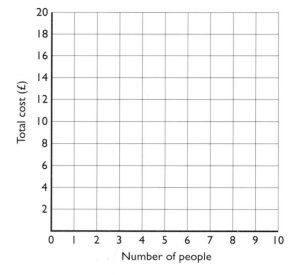

Draw a graph showing the total cost for different numbers of people to get into the amusement park.

I Question 1 is an example of **direct proportion.**

Two quantities are in direct proportion if they both go up at the same rate. For example, if one quantity is doubled so is the other.

The graph for direct proportion is always a straight line through the origin like this:

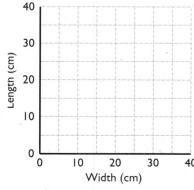

2 The area of a rectangle is 36 cm².

(a) What is the width if the length is 4 cm?

(b) What is the width if the length is 12 cm?

(c) Copy these axes.

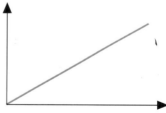

36 cm²

Draw a graph showing the width of the rectangle for different lengths.

(d) Use your graph to find the approximate width of the rectangle when the length is 7 cm.

Question 2 is an example of **inverse proportion.**

Two quantities are in inverse proportion if one goes down as the other goes up. They must both go up and down at the same rate. For example, if one quantity is doubled the other is halved.

When you multiply the two quantities together you always get the same answer.

The graph for inverse proportion always looks like this:

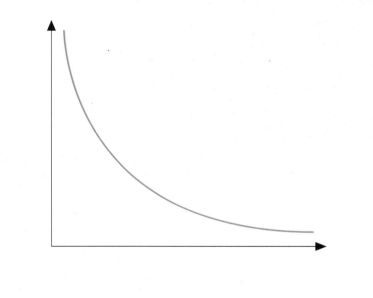

3 Some of the following are in direct proportion. Some are in inverse proportion. Some are neither. Say which is which.

(a) The number of wheels on several bicycles.

(b) The areas of rectangles of different lengths when the width is always 3 cm.

(c) The amount of pie each person gets when a pie is shared by different numbers of people.

(d) The perimeters of regular hexagons with different side lengths.

(e) The areas of equilateral triangles with different side lengths.

(f) The amount of land for each house if there are different numbers of houses to the acre.

(g) The distance of the furthest tree that can be seen from the top of a hill when different numbers of people are on the hill.

4 Some people decide to hold a disco.

The disc jockey charges £400 and provides everything necessary.

(a) How much must each ticket be sold for to cover the disc jockey's charge if:

   (i) 100 tickets are sold?
  (ii) 50 tickets are sold?
 (iii) 130 tickets are sold?
 (iv) 5 tickets are sold?

(b) Is this an example of direct or inverse proportion?

(c) Draw a graph to show the cost per ticket plotted against the number of tickets.

5 A group of people travel to an event on a train. This table shows the total cost for different numbers of people.

Number of people	Total cost
1	£4.80
2	£9.60
3	£14.40
4	£19.20
5	£24.00
6	£28.80
7	£33.60
8	£28.80
9	£32.40
10	£36.00

(a) Draw a graph of the total cost plotted against the number of people.

(b) The relationship between cost and number of people is in direct proportion to start with. When does it stop being so?

(c) Make up a story to explain the last three costs in the table.

6 Here are the average heart rates and average lifespans for different mammals:

Mammal	Heart beats per minute	Life span (years)
Ass	50	14.6
Camel	30	25
Cat	120	15
Elephant	35	24
Dog	115	15
Human	75	70
Rat	328	2.5
Tiger	64	11
Hyena	56	12
Goat	90	9

(a)

> For most mammals life span is directly proportional to heart rate.

> For most mammals life span is inversely proportional to heart rate.

Is either of the above statements true?

(b) Draw a graph of heart beats per minute plotted against life span.

(c) Which of the mammals in the table fit your graph least well?

(d) If a mammal had a heart rate of 200, what might you expect its life span to be?

■ **7** Each of the following are examples of either direct or inverse proportion. Copy each table and fill in the missing numbers.

(a)

A	3	7	9		13.5
B	7.5		22.5	30	

(b)

P	2	3		7	9.6
Q		12.3	8.7	5.3	

(c)

X	0.01	0.07		1.23	4.81
Y		254	50		3.7

D23 page 127   D24 page 128

REVIEW EXERCISES D

EXERCISE 19 Handling Data

1 Look at the pictogram on page 98.

   (*a*) How many boys spent more time watching TV?

   (*b*) How many girls spent more time listening to music?

   (*c*) What fraction of boys preferred to listen to music rather than watch TV?

2 Look at the bargraph 'Choice of music by sex' on page 99.

   (*a*) Which types of music do women like more than men?

   (*b*) What percentage of men prefer something other than pop?

   (*c*) For what type of music is there the biggest difference between men and women?

3

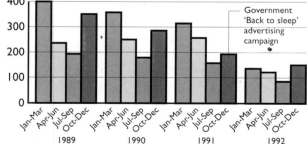

Cot deaths England and Wales, quarterly figures

When the 1992 figures were released the Government described the fall in the number of cot deaths as dramatic.

   (*a*) How many cot deaths were there in the whole of 1991?

   (*b*) How many cot deaths were there in the whole of 1992?

   (*c*) What was the percentage fall from 1991 to 1992? Is this bigger or smaller than the percentage fall from 1990 to 1991?

4 Look at the pie chart 'The growth of CDs on page 98.

Find by measuring the pie chart:

   (*a*) the percentage of sales which were CDs in 1987.

   (*b*) the percentage of sales which were CDs in 1993.

   (*c*) the ratio of LP to CD sales in 1987.

   (*d*) the ratio of LP to CD sales in 1993.

   (*e*) draw two strip charts to display the same information that the pie charts display.

5 Three people have a median age of 30, a mean age of 36 and the range of their ages is 20.

How old is each of them?

6 Three children have a mean age of 10 and the range of their ages is 6. What is the smallest possible age:

   (*a*) of the youngest child?

   (*b*) of the oldest child?

7 This pie chart shows the costs breakdown for a full-price CD in 1989/90.

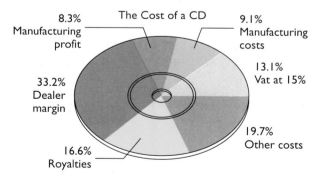

   (*a*) Was the dealer margin about a quarter, about a third, or about a half of the price of the CD?

   (*b*) These figures assumed a CD selling price of £11.49. What did this CD cost to manufacture?

   (*c*) What royalty was paid on each CD?

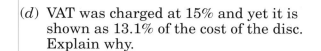

(d) VAT was charged at 15% and yet it is shown as 13.1% of the cost of the disc. Explain why.

8 Look at the frequency polygons on page 99.

(a) Calculate an estimate of the mean age of people purchasing singles.

(b) Estimate the median age of people purchasing singles.

(c) Calculate an estimate of the mean age of people purchasing albums.

(d) Estimate the median age of people purchasing albums.

(e) What conclusions can you draw from your answers to parts (a) to (d)?

EXERCISE 20 Using Numbers

1 Throughout the world 4.6 people are born every second.

(a) How many people are born every day?

(b) How many people are born every year?

2 The flood in Bangladesh in 1988 affected 37 million people, one third of the population of Bangladesh. 21 million people lost their homes.

What percentage of the population of Bangladesh lost their homes during the floods in 1988?

3 In 1993 the population of the world was 5300 million. This table shows the population of the ten largest cities.

Mexico City	21.5 million
Sao Paulo	19.9 million
Tokyo	19.5 million
New York	15.7 million
Calcutta	13.8 million
Greater Bombay	13.0 million
Shanghai	12.5 million
Seoul	12.1 million
Buenos Aires	12.0 million
Rio de Janeiro	11.9 million

(a) What percentage of the World's population live in the ten biggest cities?

(b) The population of the World's 40th biggest city is about 4 million. Estimate the percentage of the World's population which lives in the forty biggest cities.

EXERCISE 21 Graphs of Functions

1 Draw some axes with x and y both labelled from -8 to 8.

(a) On your axes draw the following graphs:

(i) $y = x + 1$

(ii) $y = x - 1$

(iii) $y = 2x + 1$

(iv) $y = 2x - 2$

(b) Which of your graphs are parallel?

(c) Which of your graphs meet on the y-axis?

(d) Which of your graphs meet on the x-axis?

2 (a) On suitably labelled axes draw graphs of $y = 2x - 3$ and $y = -x + 5$.

(b) Where do the graphs meet?

(c) Check that the coordinates of the point where the graphs meet gives the simultaneous solution of the two equations.

3 (a) On suitably labelled axes draw graphs of $y = 3x - 5$ and $x + 2y = 8$.

(b) Use your graphs to solve these two equations simultaneously.

4 (a) On suitably labelled axes draw graphs of the following:

(i) $y = x^2$

(ii) $y = x^2 + 10$

(iii) $y = 18 - x^2$

125

(b) Find the four points of intersection of the graphs.

(c) A translation maps graph (i) onto one of the other graphs. What is the vector for this translation?

(d) A reflection maps graph (i) onto one of the other graphs. What is the equation of the line of reflection?

■ 5 (a) Draw a graph of $y = \frac{1}{x}$. (Remember that x can be negative.)

(b) Where does the line $y = x$ meet $y = \frac{1}{x}$?

(c) $y = x$ is a line of symmetry of the graph $y = \frac{1}{x}$. What is the equation of the other line of symmetry?

(d) Draw the line $y = 2x$. Where does this line meet the graph of $y = \frac{1}{x}$?

■ 6 (a) Draw graphs of $y = x$, $y = x^2$, $y = x^3$ and $y = x^4$.

(b) Describe the meeting points of these four graphs.

 The steepness of a straight-line graph is often measured by its **gradient**.

$$\text{Gradient} = \frac{\textbf{Distance up}}{\textbf{Distance along}}$$

For example, here is the graph of $y = 2x + 1$.

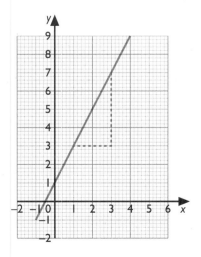

Two points on a graph are (1, 3) and (3, 7).

Between these two points the graph goes along 2 and up 4.

So the gradient of this graph is $\frac{4}{2} = 2$.

Here is the graph of $y = -3x + 4$.

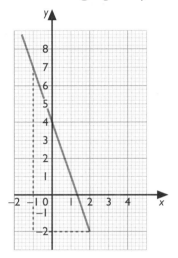

Two points on the graph are (−1, 7) and (2, −2).

Between these two points the graph goes along 3 and up −9.

So the gradient of this graph is $\frac{-9}{3} = -3$.

■ 7 (a) Find the gradient of the graph $y = 4x - 6$.

(b) Find the gradient of the graph $y = 5 - x$.

(c) A graph goes through the points (−1, 2) and (1, 7). What is its gradient?

■ 8 $y = mx + c$ is the equation of a straight line graph if m and c are given numerical values.

(a) Choose values for m and c and draw the graph of $y = mx + c$. Do this several times with different values of m and c.

(b) What does the value of m tell you about the graph?

(c) What does the value of c tell you about the graph?

EXERCISE 22 Inequalities

1 N is a positive whole number and $N \leq 5$.

Find all the possible values of N.

2 P is a positive whole number and $2P < 7$.

Find all the possible values of P.

3 Q is a whole number. $2Q < 17$ and $3Q > 7$.

Find all the possible values of Q.

4 x and y are numbers. $x \geq 0$, $x \leq 3$, $y \geq -2$ and $y \leq 2$.

(a) Find some pairs of values for x and y.

(b) Draw some axes and plot the pairs of values you found for (a).

(c) Shade the region in which (x, y) *must* lie.

5 x and y are numbers. $x \geq 0$, $y \geq 0$ and $x + 2y \leq 6$.

Draw some axes and shade the region in which (x, y) must lie.

6 (a) Find some inequalities for x and y so that the shaded region is a rhombus.

(b) Find some inequalities for x and y so that the shaded region is a kite.

EXERCISE 23 Proportion

1 A supermarket was selling Weetabix in packets of three different sizes.

12 biscuits for 65p

24 biscuits for 88p

48 biscuits for £1.73

For each packet, find the cost of one Weetabix.

2 For every 40 miles travelled in a car 1520 gallons of CO_2 are emitted.

(a) How many gallons are emitted when travelling from Leicester to Nottingham (25 miles)?

(b) How many gallons are emitted when travelling from London to Glasgow (400 miles)?

3 A car is travelling down the motorway at 70 mph.

(a) How far does it travel in 30 minutes?

(b) How long does it take to travel 10 miles?

(c) It joins the motorway at 11.37 am and travels for 137 miles on the motorway. Assuming that it can maintain a speed of 70 mph throughout its journey, at what time will it leave the motorway?

4 A supermarket was selling baked beans in tins of four different sizes:

a 220 g tin cost 22 p
a 439 g tin cost 27 p
a 587 g tin cost 43 p
an 850 g tin cost 47 p

To help shoppers decide which is the best value for money some supermarkets use unit pricing. This means that, for each tin, they would display the cost of 100g of baked beans, to the nearest 0.1p.

(a) Find the cost of 100 g of baked beans for each of the four tins.

(b) List the tins in order of value for money, giving the best value first.

(c) Are you surprised by your answer to (b)? Can you give an explanation?

(d) Is it always sensible for people to buy the 'best value' tin?

(e) One week there was a special offer on the 439 g tin.

10% extra free

The weight shown on the tin was 484 g. Was the manufacturer's claim correct?

(f) Find the cost of 100 g of beans for this special tin. Where does this tin come in your 'value for money' list?

■ **5** (a) A runner can run 100 metres in 11.4 seconds. Give his average speed in metres per second to a sensible degree of accuracy.

(b) Another runner can run a mile in 4 mins 2.7 seconds. Give his average speed in metres per second to a sensible degree of accuracy.

(c) Which of the runners is faster?

[1 metre = 1.094 yards. There are 1760 yards in a mile]

■ **6** An experimenter measures the values of A, B, C and D under different conditions. Here are his results.

A	12.2	26	39.5	63
B	5.8	2.72	1.79	1.12
C	153	33.7	14.6	5.74
D	46.7	99.6	151.3	241

(a) Which pairs of quantities are in direct proportion?

(b) Which pairs of quantities are in inverse proportion?

(c) Use your results for (a) and (b) to predict the value of two of the other quantities when B = 10.4.

(d) Look for a relationship which will help you to predict the value of the fourth quantity when B = 10.4.

EXERCISE 24 Interpreting Real-life Graphs

1

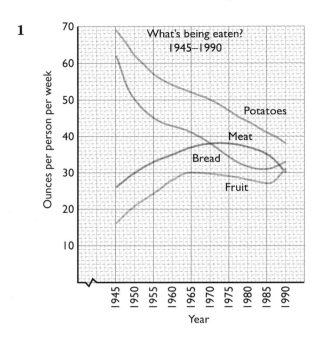

This graph shows the changes in eating habits between 1945 and 1990.

(a) In what year did people eat most fruit?

(b) In what year did people eat most meat?

(c) What weight of meat was consumed by a typical person during the whole of 1970?

(d) What weight of potatoes was consumed by a typical person during the whole of 1985?

(e) During what periods did people eat more bread than meat?

(f) What was the percentage increase in fruit consumption between 1945 and 1985?

(g) What was the percentage decrease in potato consumption between 1965 and 1985?

2

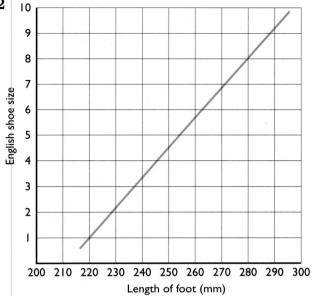

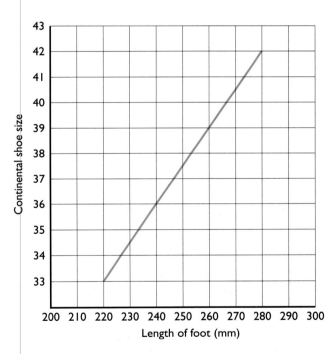

These graphs show English and continental shoe sizes.

(a) What is the length of foot suitable for a shoe of English size 6?

(b) What continental size is required for a foot of length 265 mm?

(c) What continental size would you buy if you wore English size 4 shoes?

(d) What English size would you buy if you wore continental size 40 shoes?

■ **3** A couple travel from Leicester to Cromer by car.

They start their journey at 7 a.m.

They stop for breakfast for three-quarters of an hour at 9 a.m.

They arrive at 12 noon.

When they start, their car is half full of petrol.

Immediately after breakfast they fill up the car with petrol.

While they are travelling they use up petrol at an approximately constant rate.

Draw a graph to show the amount of petrol in the tank between 6 a.m. and 1 p.m.

■ **4** Carolyn timed a ball rolling down a slope. This table shows the times the ball took to travel different distances.

Distance (cm)	Time (sec)
10	1.18
20	1.47
30	1.87
40	2.29
50	2.52
60	2.72
70	2.94
80	3.19
90	3.31
100	3.65

(a) Plot the data above as points on a graph. Plot time on the horizontal axis and distance on the vertical axis.

(b) Fit a smooth curve to the points you have plotted. (The curve should be smooth: do not draw it to pass exactly through all the points.)

(c) Is the ball slowing down or speeding up? How does the curve tell you this?

(d) What is the ball's average speed if it travels 50 cm?

(e) What is the ball's average speed if it travels 90 cm?

(f) Use your curve to predict the time taken for the ball to travel 120 cm.

IS IT POSSIBLE?

MISSING DIGITS

 Look at the following:

36 + ✳✳ = 59
4✳ + ✳8 = 93

Each star stands for a missing digit. This is what you get if you replace the missing digits:

36 + 23 = 59
45 + 48 = 93

1 Copy each of these and replace the missing digits.

(*a*) ✳✳ + 12 = 27   (*b*) 34 + 49 = ✳✳   (*c*) ✳5 + 2✳ = 78

(*d*) 3✳ + ✳6 = 51   (*e*) ✳✳ + 6 = ✳✳4

2 Copy each of these and replace the missing digits.

(*a*) 67 − 29 = ✳✳   (*b*) ✳✳ − 34 = 43

(*c*) ✳3 − 3✳ = 27   (*d*) 6 × 7 = ✳✳

(*e*) ✳ × 5 = 15   (*f*) ✳ × 7 = ✳6

(*g*) 8 × ✳ = 3✳   (*h*) ✳ × ✳ = 8✳

3 Make up some more examples like those in questions 1 and 2. Give them to someone else to solve.

 Sometimes it may *not* be possible to find digits which work. Sometimes it may be possible to find more than one answer.

For example:

2✳ × 4 = ✳5 is *not possible*
1✳ × 2 = ✳6 is *possible in two different ways*

13 × 2 = 26 or
18 × 2 = 36

In all the following questions, some examples are impossible, some can be done in only one way, and some can be done in more than one way.

4 (a) $2* \times 2 = *8$ (b) $* \times 5 = *3$ (c) $* + ** = **8$

(d) $*5 \times ** = *00$ (e) $** + ** = ****4$ (f) $*** - 1 = **$

(g) $* \times * = 49$ (h) $* \times * = 36$ (i) $* \times * = 85$

(j) $* \times ** = 145$ (k) $* \times ** = 119$ (l) $** \times ** = 544$

5 (a) Put the digits 1, 2, 3 and 4 in place of the stars. Use each digit once.

   $* \times * = **$

(b) Put the digits 1, 2, 3, 4 and 5 in place of the stars. Use each digit once.

   $* \times ** = **$

(c) Put the digits 1, 2, 3, 4, 5 and 6 in place of the stars. Use each digit once.

   $* \times ** = ***$

6 Make up some more examples like those in questions 4 and 5. Give them to someone else to solve.

 Look at this example:

$(*2)^2 = ***$

This has two possible answers:

$(12)^2 = 144$ or
$(22)^2 = 484$

> Some parts of question 7 require careful and systematic use of trial and improvement.

7 (a) $(*5)^2 = ***$ (b) $(**)^2 = **1$ (c) $(**)^2 = **8$

(d) $(**)^2 = **25$ (e) $(***)^2 = ****75$ (f) $(*)^3 = **6$

(g) $(**)^3 = ***7$ (h) $(***)^3 = 2*****3$ (i) $(***)^2 = 20***4$

(j) $(***)^2 = *44*44$ (k) $(***)^2 = *******5$ (l) $(***)^3 = *22****64$

8 Make up some more examples like those in question 7. Give them to someone else to solve.

 Look at this example:

   $*5 \div 2 = 1*.*$

This has two possible answers:

   $25 \div 2 = 12.5$ or
   $35 \div 2 = 17.5$

> **Some parts of question 9 need careful exploration if all possibilities are to be found.**

9 (a) $** \times 2.5 = 40$

(b) $** \times 0.5 = 34$

(c) $*** \times 0.2 = 23$

(d) $** \div 0.1 = 320$

(e) $** \div 0.25 = 84$

(f) $** \div 2 = 6.*$

(g) $17 \div * = *.**$

(h) $43 \div * = *.*$

(i) $2* \div 4 = *.*$

(j) $*3 \div ** = 7.*$

(k) $2* \div * = *.*$

(l) $*7 \div ** = 3.**$

(m) $* \times *.* = *6$

(n) $** \times *.* = 5$

(o) $** \div *.* = 24*$

(p) $5* \div ** = *.***$

10 Make up some more examples like those in question 9. Give them to someone else to solve.

 Look at this example:

$$\frac{*}{4} + \frac{*}{*} = \frac{7}{8}$$

This has two possible answers:

$$\frac{1}{4} + \frac{3}{8} = \frac{7}{8} \text{ or}$$

$$\frac{3}{4} + \frac{1}{8} = \frac{7}{8}$$

---

11 (a) $\dfrac{*}{2} + \dfrac{*}{*} = \dfrac{5}{8}$

(b) $\dfrac{3}{*} + \dfrac{*}{*} = \dfrac{*}{8}$

(c) $\dfrac{*}{*} + \dfrac{*}{*} = \dfrac{1}{2}$

(d) $\dfrac{*}{**} + \dfrac{*}{8} = \dfrac{3}{**}$

(e) $\dfrac{*}{*} \times \dfrac{*}{*} = \dfrac{1}{4}$

(f) $\dfrac{*}{*} \times \dfrac{*}{*} = \dfrac{1}{6}$

(g) $\dfrac{*}{*} \div \dfrac{*}{*} = \dfrac{1}{2}$

12 Make up some more examples like those in question 11. Give them to someone else to solve.

C16
page
91

E25
page
152

SQUARES, CUBES, PRIMES AND FACTORS

Some of the following are impossible, some can be done in only one way and some can be done in more than one way.

1 Make a square number from the digits 4 and 6. Use each digit once only.

2 Make a square number from the digits 1, 3 and 6. Use each digit once only.

3 Make a square number from the digits 2, 7 and 8. Use each digit once only.

4 Make two square numbers from the digits 2, 4, 5 and 6. Use each digit once only. (For example, you could make 24 and 56, except that these numbers are not squares.)

5 Make two square numbers from the digits 2, 4, 5 and 9. Use each digit once only.

6 Make a prime number from the digits 2 and 3. Use each digit once only.

7 Make a prime number from the digits 1, 2 and 5. Use each digit once only.

8 Make two prime numbers from the digits 1, 2, 3 and 4. Use each digit once only.

9 Make two prime numbers from the digits 6, 7, 8 and 9. Use each digit once only.

10 Find a prime number which is 1 less than a square number. Now find another.

11 Find a prime number which is 4 less than a square number. Now find another.

12 2 and 3 are a pair of consecutive numbers and both are prime. Find another pair of prime numbers like this.

13 3 and 5 are two apart and both are prime. Find another pair of primes like this.

14 3, 5 and 7 are three primes going up in twos. Find three more primes like this.

15 I think of a number. All except one of the numbers 1, 2, 3, 4, 5 and 6 are factors of this number.

What is the smallest number I could be thinking of?

16 I think of a number. All except two of the numbers 1, 2, 3, 4, 5, 6, 7, 8, 9 and 10 are factors of this number. The two numbers which are *not* factors are consecutive.

What is the smallest number I could be thinking of?

17 Make up some problems of your own about factors of numbers. Give them to someone else to solve.

DIFFERENT NUMBER BASES

 The number 13 in base 10 means $1 \times 10 + 3$. It is an odd number. It is also a prime.

In base 5 the number 13 means $1 \times 5 + 3$ and so it is even and a power of 2.

In base 6 the number 13 means $1 \times 6 + 3$ and so it is an odd square number.

■ **1** In which number bases is the number 32 even?

■ **2** In which number bases is the number 24 even?

■ **3** In which number bases is the number 53 even?

■ **4** In which number bases is the number 25 even?

■ **5** In which number bases is the number 23 prime?

■ **6** In which number bases is the number 31 square?

■ **7** In which number bases is the number 121 square?

■ **8** Make up your own problems about numbers' bases. Give them to someone else to solve.

F36
page
191

PAINTING CUBES

 A cube is made up of 27 small cubes.

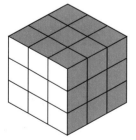

If you paint two faces of the cube as shown and then take it apart, 15 of the small cubes have paint on them.

You might find interlocking cubes useful for this activity.

1 A cube is made up of 27 small cubes. It is painted on one face. When it is taken apart how many small cubes have paint on them?

2 A cube is made up of 27 small cubes. It is painted on three faces. When it is taken apart how many small cubes have paint on them? Does it depend which three faces are painted?

3 A cube is made up of 64 small cubes. Two of its faces are painted. How many small cubes have paint on them?

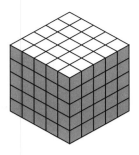

4 A cube is made up of 125 small cubes. Four of its faces are painted. How many small cubes have paint on them?

5 A cube is made up of N³ small cubes. Two of its faces are painted. How many small cubes have paint on them?

6 A cube is made up of small cubes. Some of its faces are painted. How many small cubes are in the cube if:

(a) 36 small cubes have paint on them?

(b) 200 small cubes have paint on them?

(c) 98 small cubes have paint on them?

(d) 225 small cubes have paint on them?

(e) 91 small cubes have paint on them?

(f) 120 small cubes have paint on them?

You might find *Spread* or a spreadsheet helpful for questions 6 and 7.

F35 page 190

7 Two cubes are made up of small cubes. Some of the faces of the two cubes are painted. How many small cubes are in the cubes if 81 small cubes have paint on them?

8 Make up some questions of your own about cubes and give them to someone else to answer.

TRIANGLES

> **I** For this activity a number of descriptions of triangles are given. Your task is to draw triangles with these descriptions where possible.
>
> Some descriptions are impossible.
>
> Some describe just one triangle. All the people who drew a triangle with this description would draw identical **(congruent)** triangles.
>
> Some describe more than one possible triangle.

1 A triangle with sides of length 4 cm, 5 cm and 6 cm.

2 A triangle with two sides of 5 cm and an angle of 50°.

3 A triangle with sides of 6 cm and 7 cm and an angle of 70° between these two sides.

4 A triangle with sides of length 3 cm, 5 cm and 9 cm.

5 A triangle with angles of 40°, 60° and 80°.

6 A triangle with two sides of length 5 cm and two angles of 50°.

7 A triangle with angles of 50°, 70° and 90°.

8 A triangle with sides of length 6 cm and 8 cm and an angle of 40° next to the 8 cm side, but not next to the 6 cm side.

E30 page 156

9 Make up your own descriptions of triangles.

POLYGONS

You might find *Spread*, a spreadsheet or a programmable or graphical calculator useful for questions 1(c) and 2.

■ **1** Here is a picture of a rectangle. The size of the rectangle is not known but the distances between the point P and three of the corners of the rectangle are known.

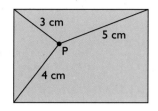
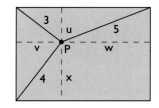

(*a*) Is it possible to find the distance between the point P and the fourth corner of the rectangle?

(*b*) Is it possible to know the lengths of the sides of this rectangle?

(*c*) Is it possible for this rectangle to be a square? If so, what is the area of this square?

■ **2** Make up your own distances instead of 3 cm, 4 cm and 5 cm. Try answering question 1 for your distances.

■ **3** A polygon is drawn inside a circle. All its angles are equal.

(*a*) If the polygon has 4 sides, is it possible that the sides are all the same length? If so, what shape is the polygon?

(*b*) If the polygon has 5 sides, is it possible that the sides are all the same length? Suppose the polygon has 6, 7, 8, ... sides?

(*c*) If the polygon has 4 sides is it possible that the sides are two different lengths? If so, what is the shape of the polygon?

(*d*) If the polygon has 5 sides is it possible that the sides are two different lengths?

(*e*) Suppose the polygon has 6, 7, 8 ... sides?

(*f*) Is it possible for the polygon to have sides of three different lengths?

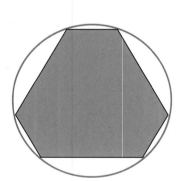

■ **4** Here is a parallelogram with its diagonals. The sizes of three angles are shown.

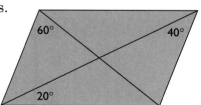

(*a*) Use the angle properties of parallel lines to calculate the four angles at the corners of the parallelogram.

(*b*) By considering the corners of the parallelogram explain why the drawing is impossible.

(*c*) The angles marked 20° and 40° are correct but the angle marked 60° is a mistake. Make an accurate drawing of the parallelogram to find what this angle should be.

E30 page 156

SEQUENCES

 Here is a simple rule for a sequence:

To find the next term of the sequence add 5.

You can have many different sequences with this rule. Here are two examples:

32, 37, 42, 47, 52, ...
15, 20, 25, 30, 35, ...

1 Here is a rule for a sequence:

To find the next term of the sequence add 4.

There are many sequences with this rule.

Is it possible to find a sequence with this rule for which

(*a*) all the numbers are even?

(*b*) all the numbers are odd?

(*c*) all the numbers are multiples of 3?

2 Here is a rule for a sequence:

To find the next term of the sequence add 3.

There are many sequences with this rule.

Is it possible to find a sequence with this rule for which

(*a*) all the numbers are even?

(*b*) all the numbers are odd?

(*c*) all the numbers are multiples of 3?

(*d*) all the numbers are multiples of 9?

(*e*) none of the numbers is a whole number?

3 Here is a rule for a sequence:

To find the next term of the sequence add 7.

There are many sequences with this rule:

(*a*) Is it possible to find a sequence with this rule where all the numbers are multiples of 7?

(*b*) Is it possible to find a sequence where none of the numbers is a whole number?

(*c*) What is the largest number of 2-digit numbers a sequence with this rule can have?

4 Here is a rule for a sequence:

To find the next term of the sequence add □.

What number could you put in the box to make the following possible?

(a) All the numbers in the sequence are even.

(b) All the numbers in the sequence are odd.

(c) All the numbers in the sequence are multiples of 3.

(d) All the numbers in the sequence end in the same digit.

(e) There are exactly ten 2-digit numbers in the sequence.

(f) Every other number in the sequence is a whole number.

(g) Every fourth number in the sequence is a whole number.

(h) Every fourth number in the sequence is a multiple of 5.

There is a simple rule for finding the next number of the sequence:

6, 10, 14, 18, 22, ...

It is possible to insert a number between each pair of numbers of the sequence, so that there is still a simple rule.

6, 8, 10, 12, 14, 16, 18, 20, 22, ...

---

5 (a) Find the next three terms of this sequence:

5, 11, 17, 23, ...

(b) Is it possible to insert a number between each pair of numbers of this sequence, so that there is still a simple rule?

6 Answer question 5 for the sequence

4, 11, 18, 25, 32, ...

7 Answer question 5 for these sequences:

(a) 5, 20, 80, 320, ...

(b) 9, 81, 729, 6561, ...

(c) 3, 6, 12, 24, 48, ...

(d) 5, −20, 80, −320, 1280, ...

(e) 2, −4, 8, −16, 32, ...

8 Can *two* numbers be inserted between each of the numbers of the following sequences?

(a) 13, 34, 55, 76, 97, ...

(b) 3, 5, 7, 9, 11, ...

(c) 3, 24, 192, 1536, ...

■ (d) 5, 10, 20, 40, ...

■ (e) 5, −40, 320, −2560, ...

■ (f) 3, −9, 27, −81, ...

F33 page 187

 One way of writing this sequence

9, 81, 729, 6561, ...

is to use indices to make the rule clear:

$9^1, 9^2, 9^3, 9^4, ...$

A number can be inserted between each pair of numbers of the sequence:

9, 27, 81, 243, 729, 2187, 6561, ...

This can still be written using indices:

$9^1, 9^{1.5}, 9^2, 9^{2.5}, 9^3, 9^{3.5}, 9^4, ...$

The rule for the sequence is still clear.

Fractions are often used instead of decimals:

$9^1, 9^{\frac{3}{2}}, 9^2, 9^{\frac{5}{2}}, 9^3, 9^{\frac{7}{2}}, 9^4, ...$

■ **9** Use the x^y button on your calculator to check that $9^{1.5}$, $9^{2.5}$, ... do give the correct numbers in the sequence in the box above.

■ **10** What do you think $9^{0.5}$ means?

Use your calculator to check.

■ **11** What numbers are the following:

(a) $16^{0.5}$ (b) $4^{0.5}$ (c) $16^{1.5}$ (d) $8^{\frac{1}{3}}$ (e) $16^{0.75}$

■ **12** Which of the following are possible? If they are possible give their values correct to two decimal places.

(a) $2^{0.5}$ (b) $5^{0.5}$ (c) $3^{1.5}$ (d) $16^{\frac{1}{3}}$

(e) $10^{\frac{2}{3}}$ (f) $(-10)^{0.5}$ (g) $(-10)^{\frac{1}{3}}$

Beware! With negative numbers some calculators will say things are impossible when they are not.

■ **13** Make up examples of your own which are *not* possible.

■ **14** Reconsider your answers to questions 7 and 8.

E26 page 152

VECTORS

> Vectors can be used to describe the sides of a shape drawn on squared paper.

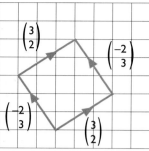

■ **1** Three of the sides of a parallelogram are $\binom{3}{4}$, $\binom{3}{4}$ and $\binom{5}{2}$.

Is this possible? If so, give the vector of the fourth side.

■ **2** For each of the following, say whether the three vectors given are three possible sides of the shape named. If they are, give the vector of the fourth side.

(a) Rhombus $\binom{2}{3}$, $\binom{2}{3}$ and $\binom{3}{2}$

(b) Trapezium $\binom{2}{4}$, $\binom{4}{8}$ and $\binom{-3}{1}$

(c) Square $\binom{1}{3}$, $\binom{1}{3}$ and $\binom{3}{-1}$

(d) Rectangle $\binom{2}{1}$, $\binom{2}{1}$ and $\binom{-2}{-4}$

(e) Rhombus $\binom{3}{4}$, $\binom{3}{4}$ and $\binom{5}{0}$

■ **3** For each of the following, say whether the two vectors given are possible diagonals of the shape named. If they are, give the vectors of the four sides. (In one case there is more than one possible answer.)

(a) Parallelogram $\binom{6}{2}$ and $\binom{2}{4}$

(b) Square $\binom{4}{2}$ and $\binom{2}{4}$

(c) Rhombus $\binom{3}{1}$ and $\binom{-2}{6}$

(d) Rectangle $\binom{5}{1}$ and $\binom{1}{5}$

(e) Kite $\binom{4}{2}$ and $\binom{-3}{6}$

LENGTH, AREA AND VOLUME

 If the length of one edge of a cube is *a*:

the total edge length is *12a*

the surface area is *6a²*

the volume is *a³*.

Some formulae for length, area and volume are not so simple. But an area is obtained by multiplying two lengths together (*a × a* in the cube example), and a volume by multiplying three lengths together (*a × a × a* in the cube example).

The circumference of a circle is *2πr* (length, so just *r*).

The area of a circle is *πr²* (area, so *r × r*).

The volume of a cylinder is *πr²h* (volume, so *r × r × h*).

■ 1 Which of these formulae give a length, which give an area, which give a volume and which are not possible for any of these?

(*a*) $2(a + b)$

(*b*) ab

(*c*) $\frac{1}{2}bh$

(*d*) $(\pi + 2)r$

(*e*) $2\pi r^2 + 2\pi rh$

(*f*) $\frac{1}{3}\pi r^2h$

(*g*) $2(ab + bc + ca)$

(*h*) $a + bc + abc$

(*i*) $\frac{\pi r^2\theta}{360}$

(*j*) $\frac{\pi r\theta}{180} + 2r$

(*k*) $a(b + c^2)$

(*l*) $\frac{1}{2}h(a + b)$

(*m*) $\frac{4\pi r^3}{3}$

(*n*) $4\pi r^2$

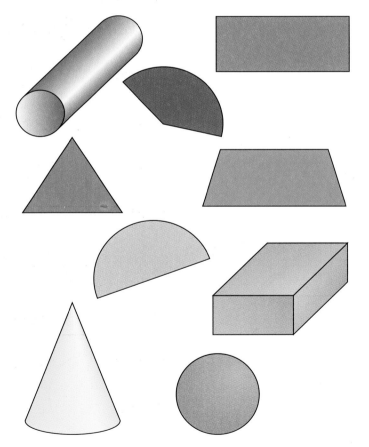

■ 2 Most of the formulae in question 1 give the lengths, areas or volumes for well-known shapes.

Identify as many of the shapes as you can.

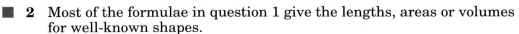

E29
page
155

141

IS IT POSSIBLE?

1 Chris has three sisters
Ann has two sisters
Ann is Chris's sister
Is this possible?

2 John is old enough to vote. His aunt is not old enough to get married. Is this possible?

3 What amounts of money is it possible to pay using exactly three different coins?

4 Two of the sides of a triangle have lengths of 4 cm and 5 cm. The area of the triangle is 10 cm². Is this possible?

Is it possible for a triangle of the same shape to have an area of exactly 40 cm²? If so, how long would its sides be?

5 A sample of people were asked whether they preferred pop music or classical music. Here are the results.

    Prefer classical   61%
    Prefer pop music   25%
    Don't know   15%

All results are correct to the nearest per cent.

But 61 + 25 + 15 = 101. Is this possible?

6 Do *not* use your calculator for this question. Use common sense and estimation to pick out the possible answer for each calculation, or say that none are possible.

(*a*) $21 \times 22 = 2122$ or 462 or 252

(*b*) $32 \times 28 = 1556$ or 606 or 896

(*c*) $26 \times 36 = 66$ or 1256 or 936

(*d*) $47 \times 59 = 3443$ or 2773 or 2887

(*e*) $254 \times 257 = 39\,228$ or $54\,548$ or $65\,278$

(*f*) $(398)^2 = 158\,402$ or $16\,344$ or $161\,484$

(*g*) $456 \times 0.48 = 218.9$ or 1636 or 322.7

(*h*) $306 \div 11 = 52.5$ or 27.8 or 11.3

(*i*) $482 \div 34 = 16.3$ or 10.3 or 14.2

(*j*) $1000 \div 127 = 7.87$ or 8.87 or 9.87

(*k*) $365 \div 0.43 = 849$ or 84.9 or 157

(*l*) $67 \div 0.083 = 87.2$ or 8.72 or 807.2

■ 7 A restaurant wants to charge exactly £4.00 for lunch, including VAT. It has to charge VAT at 17.5%. It is possible to fix the cost *without* VAT so that the cost *with* VAT is exactly £4.00?

■ 8 The price of a television is reduced by 10%. Three months later the price of the same television is increased by 10%. It does *not* return to its original price. Is this possible?

■ 9 After adding on VAT at 17.5% an item can be paid for exactly using £50 notes. If VAT was not charged, the item could be paid for exactly using £50 notes and just three coins.

   Is this possible?

■ 10 In this question all the answers are rounded to 4 significant figures and are written in standard form. The stars represent missing digits.

   Here are two numbers, p and q.

   $$p = *.*** \times 10^5$$
   $$q = *.*** \times 10^4$$

   (*a*) If $p + q = *.*** \times 10^a$ what are the possible values of a?

   (*b*) If $p - q = *.*** \times 10^b$ what are the possible values of b?

   (*c*) If $p \times q = *.*** \times 10^c$ what are the possible values of c?

   (*d*) If $p \div q = *.*** \times 10^d$ what are the possible values of d?

For question 10 you might find it helpful to experiment with numbers in standard form on your calculator.

■ 11 (*a*) A square has an area of *exactly* 64 cm².

   What is its exact perimeter?

   (*b*) Can a square have an exact area of 81 cm²? If so, what is its exact perimeter?

   (*c*) Can a square have an exact area of 32 cm²? If so, what is its exact perimeter?

E28
page
154

14 INTERSECTING CIRCLES

ARRANGEMENTS OF TWO CIRCLES

Here are some pairs of circles.

(*a*)    (*b*)    (*c*)

(*d*)    (*e*)   (*f*)

(*g*)    (*h*)    (*i*)

1 What is the same about pictures (*a*), (*b*) and (*c*)?

2 What is the same about pictures (*b*), (*f*) and (*g*)?

3 Choose other sets of pictures. Get someone else to say what is the same about them.

RED OVERLAPS

Look at these pictures of two circles.

Use the computer program *Two circles* (film 1) before answering these questions.

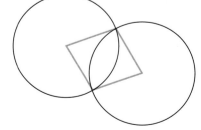   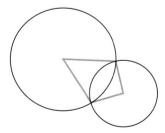

1 Describe how the red shape in each picture is drawn.

> **I** The circles can be the same size as each other or they can be different sizes.
>
> The circles can overlap a little or a lot.

You might find the resource sheet *Shapes* useful for question 2.

2 Which of the following shapes can be red shapes for two circles? Draw pictures to illustrate your answers.

(*a*) Square   (*b*) Rectangle   (*c*) Rhombus

(*d*) Parallelogram   (*e*) Trapezium   (*f*) Kite

(*g*) Arrowhead   (*h*) Isosceles triangle   (*i*) Equilateral triangle

(*j*) Scalene triangle   (*k*) Acute-angled triangle

(*l*) Right-angled triangle   (*m*) Obtuse-angled triangle.

TWO YELLOW LINES

Use the computer program *Two circles* (film 1) before answering these questions.

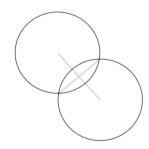
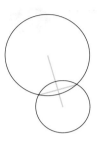

Each picture of overlapping circles has two lines drawn.

Answer the following questions

(*a*) when the two circles are the same size

(*b*) when the two circles are different sizes.

1 What is the angle between the two lines?

2 How long is one line when the other line is about to disappear?

3 What is the longest that each of the two lines can be? What is the shortest?

4 Do the two lines always intersect? If not, when do they intersect?

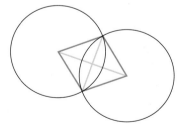
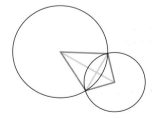

These pictures show the overlapping circles with the red shapes and the yellow lines.

5 Write down everything you can about

(*a*) the diagonals of a rhombus

(*b*) the diagonals of a square

(*c*) the diagonals of a kite.

E30
page
156

COMMON CHORDS

Use the computer program *Two circles* (film 2) to help you answer questions 1 to 6.

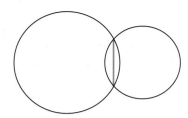

The picture above shows two circles with their common chord.

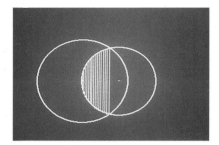

The picture above shows some of the common chords obtained when a bigger circle is dragged across a smaller circle.

In this case, the locus of the centre of the bigger circle is a line through the centre of the smaller circle.

1 What can you say about *all* the common chords in the picture above?

2 Investigate what common chords you get when a smaller circle is dragged across a bigger circle.

3 Investigate what common chords you get when a circle is dragged across another circle of the same size.

In this case the moving circle is the same size as the fixed circle. The locus of its centre is a line which is a tangent to the fixed circle.

4 How wide is the 'arch' formed by the chords in the picture on the previous page? How high is the arch?

5 Investigate the widths and heights of 'arches' which can be formed by changing the position of the moving circle so that the locus of its centre is not a tangent to the fixed circle.

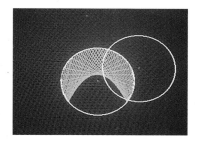

6 Investigate the widths and heights of 'arches' which can be formed by changing the size of the moving circle.

> **I** In this picture the moving circle is the same size as the fixed circle. It rotates so that its circumference always passes through the centre of the fixed circle.
>
>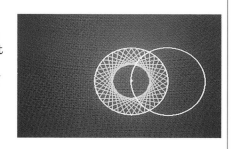

Use the computer program *Two circles* (film 3) to help you answer questions 7 to 13.

7 What is the locus of the centre of the moving circle?

8 What can you say about all the common chords in the picture above?

9 Investigate what happens if you change the size of the moving circle.

> **I** The envelope of the set of chords is the shape you can 'see' inside the chords.

10 What different sizes can the 'envelope circle' be?

If both circles are the same size, how big is the 'envelope circle'?

C15 page 90

11 How big should the moving circle be to get an envelope circle with a diameter which is two-thirds of the diameter of the fixed circle?

C18 page 92

12 How big should the moving circle be to get an envelope circle with an area which is half the area of the fixed circle?

E31 page 157

13 Investigate what happens if the circumference of the moving circle always passes through a point which is *not* the centre of the fixed circle. (Use the commands U, D, L and R in the computer program.)

A DIFFERENT CHORD

Look at this arrangement of circles.

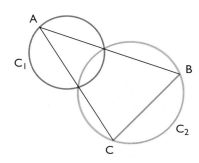

C14
page
88

■ **1** What happens to the chord BC when the point A moves round the circle C_1?

■ **2** What happens to the angle BAC when the point A moves round the circle C_1?

■ **3** Investigate what happens if you change the sizes of the two circles. Or if you change the amount by which the two circles overlap.

THREE CIRCLES

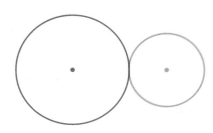

▢ **1** Two circles of radius 3 cm and 4 cm touch each other.

How far apart are their centres?

▢ **2** Three circles of radius 2 cm, 4 cm and 6 cm touch each other.

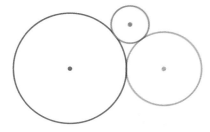

(*a*) Find the distance between each pair of centres.

(*b*) Make an accurate drawing of the three touching circles.

(*c*) What kind of triangle is formed by joining the three centres?

■ **3**

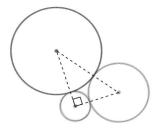

Which of these sets of circles give a right-angled triangle when the three centres are joined?

(*a*) Circles of radius 3, 4, 5   (*b*) Circles of radius 2, 3, 10

(*c*) Circles of radius 3, 5, 12   (*d*) Circles of radius 5, 12, 13

■ **4** On each of these triangles three circles are to be drawn. The centres of the circles are the vertices of the triangle. The circles are to touch each other.

Find the radii of the three circles for each triangle.

(*a*)   (*b*)   (*c*)   (*d*)

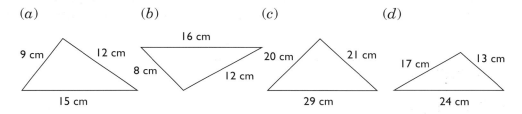

This picture shows a square with four circles. The centres of the circles are on the corners of the square. The circles touch each other.

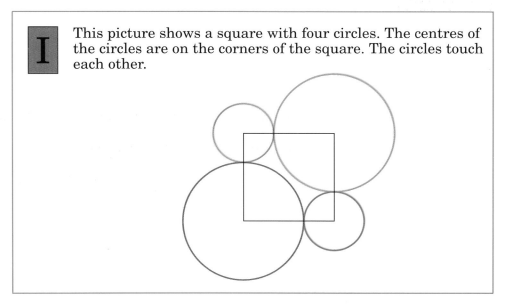

■ **5** To which of these quadrilaterals is it possible to add four circles in the same kind of arrangement as in the box above?

Where it is possible draw accurate pictures. Where it is not possible, say why not.

(*a*) Rhombus   (*b*) Rectangle   (*c*) Kite   (*d*) Parallelogram

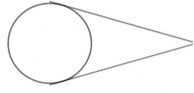

This picture shows two tangents drawn from a point to a circle.

■ **6** (*a*) What symmetry does the picture in the box above have?

(*b*) What does this tell you about the lengths of the two tangents?

■ **7** This picture shows a right-angled triangle with three circles drawn on its vertices.

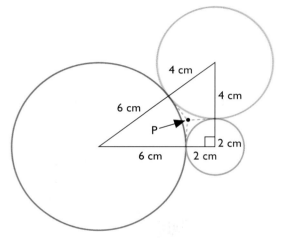

(*a*) Explain why the point P is the same distance from each side of the triangle.

(*b*) A circle is drawn to touch each side of this triangle.

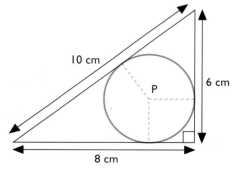

What is the radius of this circle?

■ **8** Find the radius of the circle which can be drawn in each of the following triangles.

(*a*) 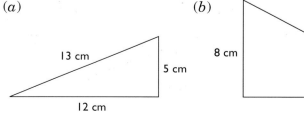   (*b*)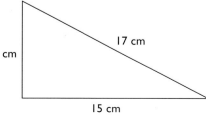

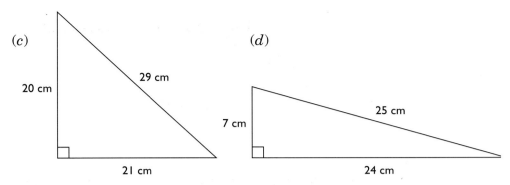

(c)

20 cm 29 cm

21 cm

(d)

7 cm 25 cm

24 cm

■ **9** The perimeter of this triangle is p and its area is A. The radius of the circle is r. Find the connection between p, r and A.

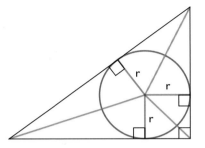

■ **10** Use the result of question 9 to check your answers to question 8.

 Here is a method of finding the area of a triangle which is not right-angled.

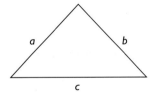

s = Semi-perimeter = $\frac{1}{2}(a + b + c)$

Area = $\sqrt{s(s - a)(s - b)(s - c)}$

■ **11** Find
   (i) the area of each triangle
   (ii) the perimeter of each triangle
   (iii) the radius of each circle.

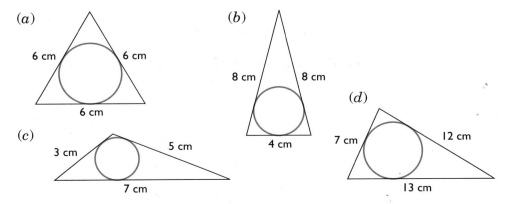

(a)

6 cm 6 cm

6 cm

(b)

8 cm 8 cm

4 cm

(c)

3 cm 5 cm

7 cm

(d)

7 cm 12 cm

13 cm

B9
page
60

E31
page
157

REVIEW EXERCISES E

EXERCISE 25 Fractions, Decimals and Percentages

> Do as many of these questions as possible without using a calculator.

1 Write these fractions in order of size, starting with the smallest:

$\frac{1}{2}, \frac{1}{8}, \frac{1}{16}, \frac{3}{8}, \frac{3}{16}, \frac{5}{8}, \frac{5}{16}, \frac{7}{8}, \frac{7}{16}, \frac{9}{16}$

2 Write these decimals in order of size, starting with the smallest:

0.5, 0.6, 0.7, 0.8, 0.9, 0.11, 0.12, 0.55, 0.155

3 Write these numbers in order of size, starting with the smallest:

5.167, 56.17, 51.67, 6.517, 1.765, 7.165,

5.617, 1.576, 67.15, $5\frac{1}{7}$, $6\frac{1}{7}$, $7\frac{1}{6}$, $56\frac{1}{7}$, $5\frac{7}{16}$

4 Write each of the following as a percentage:

(a) $\frac{3}{4}$ (b) $\frac{2}{5}$ (c) 0.4   (d) 0.83

(e) 0.475   (f) $\frac{2}{3}$ (g) $\frac{1}{6}$

5 Write each of the following as a decimal:

(a) 80%   (b) $\frac{3}{5}$ (c) $\frac{3}{8}$

(d) 65%   (e) $\frac{4}{7}$ (f) $62\frac{1}{4}\%$

6 Write each of the following as a fraction:

(a) 50%   (b) 0.3   (c) 0.6   (d) 90%

(e) 0.125   (f) 0.375   (g) 2.25

7 Find the following *without using a calculator*:

(a) 2.3 + 3.5   (b) 4.2 + 6.87

(c) 7.3 − 4.4   (d) 12.5 − 8.92

(e) 2.4 × 3   (f) 4.7 × 7

(g) 13.2 × 17   (h) 4.5 ÷ 3

(i) 5.6 ÷ 8   (j) 1.44 ÷ 12

(k) 1.2 ÷ 30

8 Find the following *without using a calculator*:

(a) 40 × 0.2   (b) 60 × 0.03

(c) 40 ÷ 0.2   (d) 60 ÷ 0.03

9 (a) Find the following

(i) $\frac{1}{3} + \frac{1}{6}$ (ii) $\frac{1}{3} - \frac{1}{6}$

(iii) $\frac{2}{3} + \frac{5}{6}$ (iv) $\frac{5}{6} - \frac{2}{3}$

(v) $\frac{1}{3} + \frac{1}{12}$ (vi) $\frac{1}{3} - \frac{1}{12}$

(vii) $\frac{7}{12} - \frac{1}{6}$ (viii) $\frac{7}{12} + \frac{1}{6}$

(b) List your answers to part (a) in order of size, starting with the smallest.

10 11 ÷ 4 = 2.75

Copy and complete the following. Each star represents a digit. All answers are exact.

(a) 17 ÷ 4 = *.**   (b) 19 ÷ * = *.*

(c) 89 ÷ * = **   (d) 13 ÷ * = *.***

(e) 42 ÷ * = *.**   (f) 62 ÷ ** = *.****

11 The reciprocal of 4 is $\frac{1}{4}$ = 0.25 and of 7 is $\frac{1}{7}$ = 0.1429 (correct to 4 significant figures).

(a) What is the reciprocal of

(i) 5?   (ii) 50?   (iii) 3?

(iv) 0.3?   (v) 27?   (vi) 0.0027?

(b) The reciprocal of a whole number between 0 and 100 is 0.02*26, correct to 4 significant figures. Find the number.

(c) The reciprocal of a whole number between 100 and 1000 is 0.0012**5, correct to 5 significant figures. Find the number.

EXERCISE 26 Indices and Standard Form

■ **1** Find the following

(a) 2^2 (b) 3^3 (c) $9^{\frac{1}{2}}$ (d) $25^{\frac{1}{2}}$

(e) $27^{\frac{1}{3}}$ (f) $625^{\frac{1}{4}}$ (g) $64^{\frac{2}{3}}$ (h) $36^{1.5}$

I Look at this sequence:

| 81 | , | 27 | , | 9 | , | 3 | , | 1 | , | $\frac{1}{3}$ | , | $\frac{1}{9}$ | , | $\frac{1}{27}$ | ... |
| 3^4 | , | 3^3 | , | 3^2 | , | 3^1 | , | 3^0 | , | 3^{-1} | , | 3^{-2} | , | 3^{-3} | ... |

This explains the meaning of negative indices.

■ **2** Find the following:

(a) 2^{-2} (b) 3^{-3} (c) 5^{-1} (d) 11^0

(e) $16^{-\frac{1}{2}}$ (f) $27^{-\frac{2}{3}}$ (g) $256^{-\frac{3}{4}}$ (h) $9^{-2.5}$

■ **3** How many seconds are there in 32 years?

■ **4** (a) Mercury is 3.6×10^7 miles from the Sun. It takes 88 days to circle the Sun. Assuming that its orbit is a circle, find in miles per hour the speed it travels at.

(b) Jupiter is 4.84×10^8 miles from the Sun. It circles the Sun at 2.92×10^4 miles per hour. Assuming that its orbit is a circle, find in years the time it takes to circle the Sun.

(c) Pluto takes 248 years to circle the Sun at a speed of 1.06×10^4 miles per hour. How far is it from the Sun?

■ **5** Assuming that human hair grows at the rate of about half an inch in a month, how fast does hair grow in miles per hour? Give your answer in standard form.

[There are 12 inches in a foot, 3 feet in a yard, and 1760 yards in a mile.]

■ **6** (a) A snail travels at 25 feet per hour. What is its speed in miles per second?

(b) The Sun is 93 million miles from the Earth. What is the Earth's speed around the sun in miles per second?

(c) Find the ratio of the snail's speed to the Earth's speed.

EXERCISE 27 Vectors

■ **1** Step A is the vector $\binom{2}{1}$ and step B is the vector $\binom{1}{3}$.

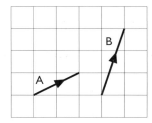

(a) What vector represents step A followed by step B? This step could be written AB.

(b) What step represents ABA?

(c) What vector represents the step that would return an object to its starting point after the step ABABB?

(d) What combinations of steps A and B will produce a step with vector $\binom{13}{19}$?

2 The vector $\begin{pmatrix} 2 \\ 4 \end{pmatrix}$ is one side of an isosceles triangle.

Which of the following vectors could be one of the other sides of the triangle?

(a) $\begin{pmatrix} 4 \\ 0 \end{pmatrix}$ (b) $\begin{pmatrix} 0 \\ 4 \end{pmatrix}$ (c) $\begin{pmatrix} 6 \\ 0 \end{pmatrix}$ (d) $\begin{pmatrix} 0 \\ 6 \end{pmatrix}$

(e) $\begin{pmatrix} 8 \\ 0 \end{pmatrix}$ (f) $\begin{pmatrix} 0 \\ 8 \end{pmatrix}$ (g) $\begin{pmatrix} 1 \\ 3 \end{pmatrix}$ (h) $\begin{pmatrix} -1 \\ 3 \end{pmatrix}$

3 Five squares have the following vectors for one of their sides:

A: $\begin{pmatrix} 2 \\ 3 \end{pmatrix}$ B: $\begin{pmatrix} 4 \\ 0 \end{pmatrix}$ C: $\begin{pmatrix} 2 \\ 2 \end{pmatrix}$ D: $\begin{pmatrix} -4 \\ 1 \end{pmatrix}$ E: $\begin{pmatrix} 5 \\ 0 \end{pmatrix}$

(a) Arrange these squares in order of size, starting with the smallest.

(b) Find the vectors for the diagonals for each of these squares.

(c) One of the diagonals of a sixth square is the vector $\begin{pmatrix} 7 \\ 3 \end{pmatrix}$. Find a vector for one side of the square.

4 Here are some vectors:

$\mathbf{a} = \begin{pmatrix} 3 \\ 4 \end{pmatrix}$, $\mathbf{b} = \begin{pmatrix} 5 \\ 0 \end{pmatrix}$, $\mathbf{c} = \begin{pmatrix} 4 \\ -3 \end{pmatrix}$,

$\mathbf{d} = \begin{pmatrix} -8 \\ 6 \end{pmatrix}$, $\mathbf{e} = \begin{pmatrix} 3 \\ -4 \end{pmatrix}$

(a) Which two of these vectors could be two sides of a square?

(b) Which two of these vectors could be two sides of a rhombus?

(c) Which two of these vectors could be two sides of a rectangle?

(d) Which three of these vectors could be three sides of an isosceles trapezium?

EXERCISE 28   Using Percentages

1

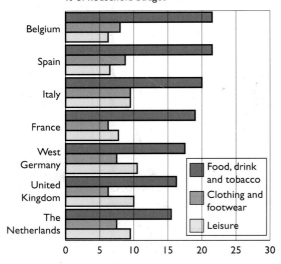

European lifestyles
Household spending patterns 1992
% of household budget

(a) In which country do people spend the highest percentage of their income on food, drink and tobacco?

(b) In which country do people spend the highest percentage of their income on leisure?

(c) In which country do people spend the lowest percentage of their income on clothing and footwear?

(d) Why does the answer to (c) *not* tell you in which country people spend least on clothing and footwear?

2

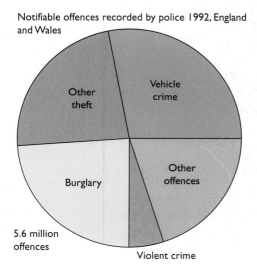

Notifiable offences recorded by police 1992, England and Wales

(a) By measuring the appropriate angle on the pie chart find what percentage of notifiable offences were violent crimes in 1992.

(b) Find what percentage of notifiable offences were vehicle crimes in 1992.

(c) How many burglaries were notified in 1992?

3 Of the 470 high court judges in 1988, 16 were women. In 1981 it was 10 out of 411. In which of these two years was there a higher percentage of women high court judges?

4 In 1988 62% of girls left school with at least one GCSE with grade C or above, compared to 54% of boys.

Assuming that half of the 600 000 young people who left school in 1988 were boys, how many more girls than boys left school with at least one GCSE with grade C or above?

5 Here are the prices of some packets of digestive biscuits.

McVitie digestives	Tesco digestives
McVitie digestives 25% EXTRA FREE 400 g 57p	TESCO DIGESTIVES 400 g 52p
20% EXTRA FREE McVitie digestives 500 g 63p	TESCO DIGESTIVES 500 g 57p

(a) Which 400 g pack is the best buy?

(b) Which 500 g pack is the best buy?

(c) Which is the best buy overall?

6 A Gallup survey in 1992 questioned 401 mothers with babies under 18 months.

(a) 44 per cent of the mothers questioned had two children. How many mothers was that?

(b) 76 per cent of the mothers were married. How many mothers was that?

(c) 50 per cent of the mothers between 16 and 24 were married. How many mothers was that?

(d) 3 per cent of the mothers surveyed chose a walk in the park as the occasion to tell their partners that they were pregnant. How many mothers was that?

(e) Items such as prams and cots cost £74.97 per month, an increase of £4.77 on the previous year. What percentage increase was that?

(f) The survey found that 2 out of 3 mothers would choose to stay at home if they could afford to, but 40 per cent went back to work within three months.

What percentage of mothers who go back to work would stay at home if they could afford to do so?

7

Each of these special packs contains three rolls of mints.

(a) The normal size roll contains 17 mints. How many mints are there in the roll which is 23% bigger?

(b) Each bigger roll contains 53 g of mints. What is the weight of mints in the normal size rolls?

8 VAT at 17.5% is added to a phone bill. What percentage of the *total* phone bill is VAT?

9 In 1970 about a third of the World's tropical rain forests had already been destroyed. About 100 000 square kilometres were being lost each year. This was 0.5 per cent of the remainder.

   (*a*) What was the original area of the tropical rain forests?

   (*b*) By 1990 about 170 000 square kilometres of rain forests were being lost each year. Estimate what percentage this is of the remaining rain forests.

EXERCISE 29   Units and Dimensions

1 What units would be used to measure

   (*a*) the length of a classroom?

   (*b*) the distance between your house and school?

   (*c*) the length of the coastline of Britain?

   (*d*) the area of your desk top?

   (*e*) the area of your school grounds?

   (*f*) the area of Britain?

   (*g*) the weight of a letter?

   (*h*) the weight of a lorry?

   (*i*) the weight of a bag of potatoes?

   (*j*) the volume of liquid you drink in a day?

   (*k*) the volume of water your house uses in a day?

   (*l*) the volume of spice added when cooking?

2 Complete the following statements.

   (*a*) There are ___ centimetres in a metre.

   (*b*) There are ___ grams in a kilogram.

   (*c*) There are ___ millimetres in a centimetre.

   (*d*) There are ___ centimetres in a kilometre.

   (*e*) There are ___ square centimetres in a square metre.

   (*f*) There are ___ cubic centimetres in a cubic metre.

   (*g*) There are ___ square inches in a square foot.

   (*h*) There are ___ inches in a mile.

   (*i*) There are ___ cubic feet in a cubic yard.

   (*j*) There are ___ grams in a tonne.

   [1 tonne = 1000 kg, 1 mile = 1760 yards, 1 yard = 3 feet, 1 foot = 12 inches]

3 Which of the following formulae are formulae for length, which for area and which for volume:

   (*a*) $4M + 2N + 2P$

   (*b*) $MN + MP + M^2$

   (*c*) $\frac{1}{2}bh$

   (*d*) $b + 2\sqrt{\frac{b^2}{4} + \frac{h^2}{2}}$

   (*e*) $\frac{\sqrt{3}}{2}a^2$

   (*f*) $4a$

   (*g*) $2(MN + MP + P^2) + Q(4M + 2N + 2P)$

   (*h*) $Q(MN + MP + P^2)$

4 Ben was investigating triangles drawn on isometric dot paper. He obtained this formula for the areas of his triangles.

   $$m^2 + mn^2 + n^2$$

Sarah looked at this formula and said, 'That can't be right!'

How did she know?

EXERCISE 30   Classifying and Defining Shapes

1 You tell a group of people to draw a square. What else do you have to tell them to be sure that they all draw the same square (if they follow your instructions carefully)?

2 You tell a group of people to draw a rectangle. What else do you have to tell them to be sure that they all draw the same rectangle?

3 (*a*) Answer question 1, but for a circle instead of a square.

    (*b*) Answer question 1, but for an isosceles triangle.

    (*c*) Answer question 1, but for a regular octagon.

■ **4** Here is a list of types of triangle:

    equilateral triangle
    isosceles triangle
    scalene triangle
    acute-angled triangle
    right-angled triangle
    obtuse angled triangle

The following is a list of statements about triangles. For each statement, put its letter against one of the types of triangle as long as you are *sure* that what is being described *has* to be this type of triangle.

For example, look at the first statement (A) below. You put A against *isosceles triangle,* because you know that a triangle with a line of symmetry *has to be* isosceles. You do *not* put A against equilateral triangle, because although a triangle with a line of symmetry *might* be equilateral, it does not *have* to be.

Copy the list of triangles above and write the appropriate letters beside them.

(A) The triangle has a line of symmetry.

(B) The triangle has no symmetry.

(C) The triangle has a line of symmetry and one of its angles is 70°.

(D) When a circle is drawn through the three corners of the triangle, the centre of the circle is on one of the sides of the triangle.

(E) The triangle can be cut into two pieces. Both these pieces are the same shape as the original triangle.

■ **5** Here is a list of types of quadrilateral:

    rhombus
    parallelogram
    kite
    square
    rectangle
    trapezium
    isosceles trapezium

Below there is a list of statements about quadrilaterals. For each statement, put its letter against one of the types of quadrilateral as long as you are *sure* that what is being described *has* to be this type of quadrilateral.

(A) The quadrilateral has four equal angles.

(B) The diagonals meet at their midpoints.

(C) The diagonals are the same length.

(D) The diagonals cut all the corner angles exactly in half.

(E) The diagonals meet at 90°.

(F) One pair of sides is parallel.

(G) The diagonals are the same length and meet exactly at their centres.

(H) The diagonals meet at 90°, and cut all the corner angles exactly in half.

(I) The diagonals meet at 90°, and the meeting point is at the centre of one of the diagonals.

(J) The diagonals are the same length and two sides are parallel.

■ **6** You have a scalene triangle drawn on a piece of paper in front of you. You want someone at the other end of a telephone to draw the same triangle. What could you tell them about the triangle to be sure that they do this?

There are several possible answers. Find as many of them as possible. In each case give the *least* amount of information necessary to get them to draw the correct triangle.

■ **7** Someone says: If you know any three things about a triangle you can draw it accurately.

Explain why this is not true.

EXERCISE 31 Properties of Circles

■ **1** A regular hexagon is drawn inside a circle with radius 5 cm.

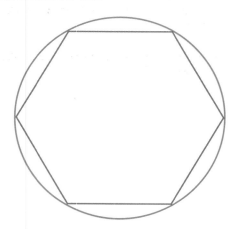

What is the perimeter of the hexagon?

■ **2** A square is drawn inside a circle with radius 8 cm.

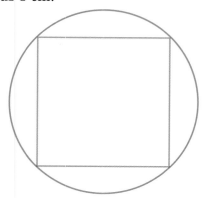

(*a*) What is the perimeter of the square?

(*b*) What is the area of the square?

■ **3**

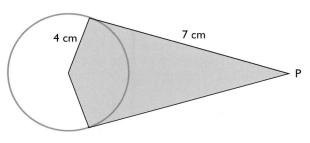

The lengths of the tangents from the point P to the circle are 7 cm. The radius of the circle is 4 cm.

Find the area of the kite shaded.

■ **4** The point Q is 15 cm from the centre of the circle. The diameter of the circle is 18 cm.

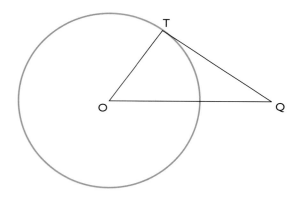

Find the distance QT.

■ **5**

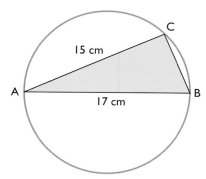

AB is a diameter of a circle. The length of AB is 17 cm. AC is a chord with length 15 cm.

Find the area of triangle ABC.

6 This picture shows a chord of length 8 cm drawn inside a circle of radius 5 cm.

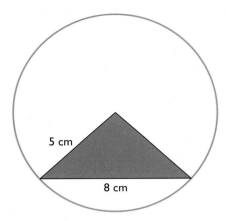

5 cm

8 cm

Find the area of the blue triangle.

7 The radius of the circle is 13 cm. The length of chord AB is 10 cm. Find the area of the green region.

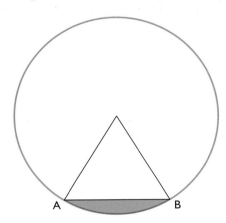

A   B

8 A regular pentagon is drawn round the outside of a circle of radius 10 cm, as shown.

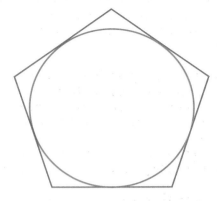

Find the perimeter of the pentagon.

Compare this with the circumference of the circle.

9 A rod of length 1 metre has a handkerchief tied to the middle of it. Two people carry the rod so that the handkerchief moves in a circle with radius 1 metre and the rod is a tangent to this circle.

What is the shape and size of the locus of one of the people?

15 AT RANDOM

COMPLETING THE QUESTIONNAIRE

For this activity you will need the resource sheet *Random questionnaire.*

When something is chosen at random it means that all the possible choices are equally likely to be chosen.

How good are human beings at choosing things at random? To help you find out answer the questions on the resource sheet called *Random questionnaire.* It is best if the whole class does this at the same time.

You can then find out how good you, and other people in the class are at being random.

CHOOSING A NUMBER AT RANDOM

Collect all the numbers chosen by people in the class for question 1 of the *Random questionnaire.* Organise them in a sensible way.

What do you notice about the random choices people have made?

Are people good at choosing at random?

CHOOSING A PAGE AT RANDOM

Collect all the page numbers people in the class chose for question 2 of the *Random questionnaire.*

Organise them in a sensible way. You could group them using class intervals, for example.

What do you notice about the random choices people have made?

What would you expect to happen if the choices really were random?

CHOOSING DIGITS AT RANDOM

 Look at the three digits you chose at random (question 3 on the random questionnaire). Suppose they were 5, 7 and 8. You could put them together in different ways to make a 3-digit number.

You could make 578 or 785 or 758 or ...

1 Use the three digits you chose.

(*a*) Can you make a 3-digit number from them which is even?

(*b*) Can you make a 3-digit number from them which is a multiple of 3?

(c) Can you make a 3-digit number from them which is a multiple of 4?

(d) Of 5?

(e) Of 6?

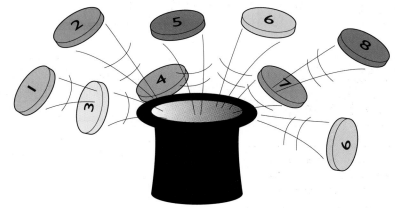

For question 2 you need a calculator or a computer that can pick random numbers or else you need ten playing cards numbered 1 to 10.

2 Get a computer or calculator to pick three digits at random (or else use some playing cards). Use these three digits.

(a) Can you make a 3-digit number from them which is even?

(b) Can you make a 3-digit number from them which is a multiple of 3?

(c) Can you make a 3-digit number from them which is a multiple of 4?

(d) Of 5?

(e) Of 6?

3 (a) Collect together the answers to questions 1 and 2 for the whole class.

Theoretical probabilities for being able to form multiples of different numbers from three digits picked at random.

Multiple	Probability
2	0.87
3	0.33
4	0.64
5	0.49
6	0.29

Probabilities are given correct to two decimal places.

F32 page 186

F36 page 191

(b) Compare the answers you have collected with the theoretical probabilities shown in the box.

(c) Discuss whether the digits chosen by people in your class are more or less random than the numbers picked by using a computer, a calculator or playing cards.

CALCULATING PROBABILITIES FOR DIGITS

In the previous activity a table of probabilities was provided. This activity provides you with the opportunity to work out these probabilities for yourself.

> **Firstly, we consider the probability of being able to make an even number from three digits picked at random.**

1 (a) How many odd digits are there?

(b) How many even digits are there?

(c) A digit is picked at random. What is the probability that it is even?

2 You pick two digits at random.

(a) How would you decide whether an even number could be made from your two digits?

(b) Suppose you see how many of your two digits are even.

There are four possibilities for choosing your two digits.

odd followed by **odd**
odd followed by **even**
even followed by **odd**
even followed by **even**

Is each of these four possibilities equally likely?

(c) What is the probability of being able to make an even number from two digits picked at random?

3 You pick three digits at random.

(a) How would you decide whether an even number could be made from your three digits?

(b) Suppose you see how many of your digits are even.

This time there are eight possibilities. List them.

(c) Is each of these eight possibilities equally likely?

(d) What is the probability that you will be able to make an even number from three digits picked at random?

> **We now consider the probability of being able to make a multiple of 5 from three digits picked at random.**

4 (a) If a number is a multiple of 5 what digit does it end in?

(b) A digit is picked at random. What is the probability that it is a suitable digit for a multiple of 5 to end in?

Two digits are picked at random.

A tree diagram can be used to describe the possibilities. S means the digit is suitable for a multiple of 5 to end in. N means that it is not suitable.

The tree diagram shows picking the first digit and then the second digit.

The probabilities have been marked on the branches of the tree diagram.

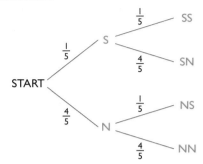

To find the probability of getting from the start to SS you multiply the probabilities on the branches.

The probability of getting to SS is $\frac{1}{5} \times \frac{1}{5} = 0.04$

The probability of getting to SN is $\frac{1}{5} \times \frac{4}{5} = 0.16$

The probability of getting to NS is $\frac{4}{5} \times \frac{1}{5} = 0.16$

The probability of getting to NN is $\frac{4}{5} \times \frac{4}{5} = 0.64$

To find the probability of getting what you want (at least one suitable digit) you add the probabilities.

The probability of getting at least *one* suitable digit is $0.04 + 0.16 + 0.16 = 0.36$.

So the probability of being able to arrange two random digits so as to get a multiple of 5 is 0.36.

5 Three digits are picked at random.

(*a*) Copy this tree diagram for the possibilities.

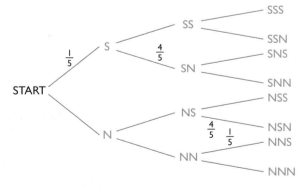

(*b*) Put the probabilities on the branches of the tree diagram. Some have been done for you.

(*c*) Find the probability that at least one of the three digits is suitable.

(*d*) What is the probability of being able to arrange three random digits so as to get a multiple of 5?

> We now consider the probability of being able to make a multiple of 4 from three digits picked at random.

■ **6** (*a*) What type of digit does a multiple of 4 end in?

(*b*) If a multiple of 4 ends in 2 or 6, what can you say about the digit next to it?

(*c*) If a multiple of 4 ends in 0, 4 or 8, what can you say about the digit next to it?

■ **7** In question 2(*b*) there is a list of the four possibilities for two digits picked at random.

(*a*) What is the probability that both digits are even?

(*b*) What is the probability that one of the digits is even?

(*c*) What is the probability that neither of the digits is even?

■ **8** In question 3(*b*) you listed the possibilities for three digits picked at random.

(*a*) What is the probability that all three digits are even?

(*b*) What is the probability that two of the digits are even?

(*c*) What is the probability than one of the digits is even?

(*d*) What is the probability that none of the digits is even?

 We could use a tree diagram to help us find the probability of being able to make a multiple of 4 from *two* digits picked at random.

We start with how many even digits we pick.

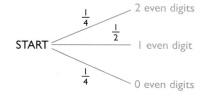

We then complete the tree diagram like this.

YES means we can make a multiple of 4. NO means we can't.

We need to know what probabilities to put in place of the question marks.

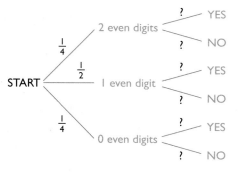

■ **9** If neither of the two digits is even what is the probability that you can make a multiple of 4 with the digits?

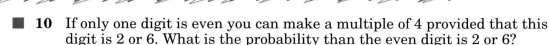

■ 10 If only one digit is even you can make a multiple of 4 provided that this digit is 2 or 6. What is the probability than the even digit is 2 or 6?

■ 11 If both digits are even you can make a multiple of 4 *unless* both digits are 2 or 6.

    (*a*) What is the probability that the first even digit is 2 or 6?

    (*b*) What is the probability that the second even digit is a 2 or 6?

    (*c*) To find the probability that *both* even digits are 2 or 6 we multiply the answer to (*a*) by the answer to (*b*).

What is the probability that both even digits are 2 or 6?

 The tree diagram can now be completed using the answers to questions 9, 10 and 11.

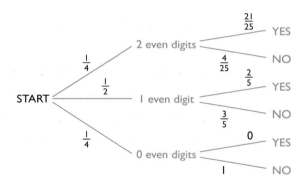

The probability of getting a multiple of 4 when you pick two digits is therefore $\frac{1}{4} \times \frac{21}{25} + \frac{1}{2} \times \frac{2}{5} = 0.41$.

■ 12 Suppose you pick three digits at random and they are all odd. What is the probability that you can make a multiple of 4 from them?

■ 13 Suppose you pick three digits at random and just one of them is even.

    (*a*) What must the even digit be if a multiple of 4 is to be formed?

    (*b*) What is the probability that you will get this even digit?

■ 14 Suppose you pick three digits at random and two of them are even. What is the probability that you will be able to form a multiple of 4? (Use your answer to question 6.)

■ 15 Suppose you pick three digits at random and they are all even. You will be able to form a multiple of 4 provided that they are not *all* 2 or 6.

What is the probability that they are *all* 2 or 6?

■ **16** Here is a tree diagram which can be used to find the probability that three digits chosen at random can be arranged to form a multiple of 4.

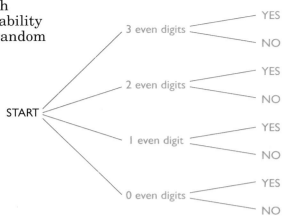

(a) Copy the diagram.

(b) Put in the probabilities on the branches. (To do this, use the answers to questions 8, 12, 13, 14 and 15.)

(c) Work out the probability of being able to make a multiple of 4 from three random digits.

> **We now consider the probability of being able to make a multiple of 3 from three digits picked at random.**

■ **17** (a) How many multiples of three are there up to and including 999? Count 0 as a multiple of 3.

(b) What is the probability that a number picked at random between 0 and 999 is a multiple of 3?

(c) If three digits make a multiple of 3 it does not matter how they are arranged. What is the probability that three digits picked at random make a multiple of 3?

F32
page
186

CHOOSING SQUARES AT RANDOM

For question 2 you need a calculator or a computer that can pick random numbers. Or else you need some playing cards.

1 Look at the three squares you chose at random (question 4 on the random questionnaire).

How many of the squares you chose are boundary squares (red squares in the picture)?

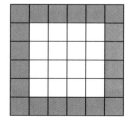

2 Get a computer or calculator to pick three squares at random (or else use some playing cards). You will need to think how to do this.

How many of the squares picked are boundary squares this time?

3 (a) Collect together the results for questions 1 and 2 for the whole class. Comment on any differences you notice in the results.

Theoretical probabilities for the number of boundary squares obtained when three squares are picked at random from a 6 by 6 grid.

Number of boundary squares	Probability
0	0.08
1	0.34
2	0.43
3	0.16

(b) Compare the answers you have collected with the theoretical probabilities shown in the box.

(c) Discuss whether the squares chosen by people in your class are more or less random than the squares picked by a computer, a calculator or playing cards.

CALCULATING PROBABILITIES FOR SQUARES

■ **1** (a) How many boundary squares are there on a 6 by 6 grid?

(b) If a square is picked at random what is the probability that it is a boundary square?

 Here is a tree diagram for calculating the probability of getting different numbers of boundary squares when three squares are picked at random.

B means a boundary square:
N means a square which is not a boundary square.

Some of the probabilities have been put on the branches.

The explanation for $\frac{19}{35}$ is that once a boundary square has been picked, there are 35 squares left and 19 of them are boundary squares.

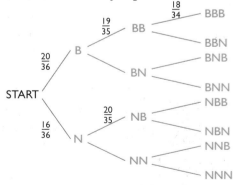

■ **2** (a) Copy the tree diagram in the box above.

(b) Complete the tree diagram by putting the probabilities on all the branches.

(c) When three squares are picked at random what is the probability of getting

    (i) no boundary squares?   (iii) two boundary squares?
    (ii) one boundary square?   (iv) three boundary squares?

F32
page
186

CHOOSING DOTS AT RANDOM

For question 2 you need a calculator or a computer that can pick random numbers. Or else you need some playing cards.

1 Look at the three dots you chose at random (question 5 on the random questionnaire).

Are the three dots in a straight line?

2 Get a computer or a calculator to pick three dots at random (or else use some playing cards). You will need to think how to do this.

Are these three dots in a straight line?

3 (a) Collect together the results for questions 1 and 2 for the whole class.

(b) The probability of getting three dots in a line if the dots are picked at random is 0.10.

Are people better or worse than a computer, calculator or playing cards, at choosing dots at random?

CALCULATING PROBABILITIES FOR DOTS

 To calculate probabilities for dots we need to know how many different sets of three dots can be chosen.

There are 9 ways of picking the first dot.

There are 8 ways of picking the second dot.

There are 7 ways of picking the third dot.

A●   B●   C●

D●   E●   F●

G●   H●   I●

So altogether there are $9 \times 8 \times 7 = 504$ ways of picking three dots.

But each set of three dots can be picked in six different ways.

For example the set of dots ACH can be picked as:

ACH   CHA
AHC   HAC
CAH   HCA

■ **1** It was explained in the box opposite that there are 504 ways of picking three dots, but that each set of three dots can be picked in six different ways.

So how many sets of three dots are there?

■ **2** What is the probability of picking a particular set of three dots?

■ **3** How many sets of three dots are in a straight line?

■ **4** What is the probability of picking three dots in a straight line?

■ **5** Nine dots do not have to be arranged in three rows of three. There are many other ways of arranging nine dots.

Here are two other arrangements.

Whatever arrangement you use, people could be asked to choose three dots at random.

(*a*) What is the best way of arranging nine dots so that the probability of the three chosen dots being in a line is as high as possible?

(*b*) What is the best way of arranging nine dots so that the probability of the three chosen dots being in a line is as low as possible?

(*c*) Look at other ways of arranging the dots. For each way find the probability that three dots chosen at random are in a straight line.

■ **6** Devise a different probability experiment for choosing dots at random.

For example, you could still use the three by three grid but get everyone to choose four dots. You could then find the probability of four dots forming a rectangle.

There are lots of other possibilities.

You could use three dots and work out the area of the triangle they form.

You could use five dots.

You could use two dots and think of a test for them.

F32
page
186

16 FITTING SHAPES

FITTING SQUARES INTO SQUARES

You will need squared paper for this activity.

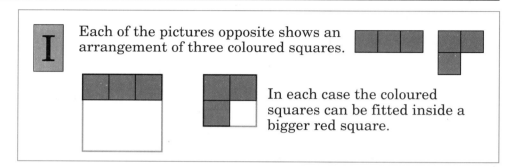

I Each of the pictures opposite shows an arrangement of three coloured squares.

In each case the coloured squares can be fitted inside a bigger red square.

1 Look at the two red squares in the box above.

(a) What fraction of each red square is coloured?

(b) What percentage of each red square is coloured?

2 Here are two arrangements of eight coloured squares:

(a) Copy these arrangements.

(b) Draw a square round each arrangement.

(c) What fraction of each square you drew for (b) is coloured?

(d) What percentage of each square you drew for (b) is coloured?

3 (a) Draw two arrangements of 12 coloured squares.

(b) Draw a square round each arrangement.

(c) What fraction of each square you drew for (b) is coloured?

(d) What percentage of each square you drew for (b) is coloured?

4 These pictures show how to position 1, 2, 3 and 4 squares so that the square you can put round them is as *small* as possible.

(a) What fraction of each red square is coloured?

(b) What percentage of each red square is coloured?

Number of squares coloured	Percentage of big square coloured
1	100
2	
3	75
4	
5	
6	
7	
8	89
9	
10	

5 (*a*) Arrange 5, 6, 7, 8, 9 and 10 squares so that the square you put round them is as small as possible.

(*b*) Copy and complete this table.

E25
page
152

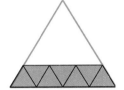

FITTING TRIANGLES INTO TRIANGLES

You will need isometric line paper for this activity.

1 These pictures show two arrangements of seven triangles fitted inside a red triangle.

(*a*) What fraction of the red triangle is filled by the seven triangles?

(*b*) What percentage of the red triangle is filled by the seven triangles?

2 These pictures show how to position 1, 2, 3 and 4 triangles so that the triangle you can put round them is as small as possible.

(*a*) What fraction of each red triangle is coloured?

(*b*) What percentage of each red triangle is coloured?

3 (*a*) Arrange 5, 6, 7, 8, 9 and 10 triangles so that the triangle you put round them is as small as possible.

(*b*) Copy and complete this table.

Number of triangles coloured	Percentage of big triangle coloured
1	
2	50
3	
4	
5	
6	
7	
8	
9	100
10	

171

FITTING HEXAGONS INTO HEXAGONS

You will need isometric line paper for this activity.

1 Here is an arrangement of three regular hexagons.

(a) Copy this arrangement onto isometric paper.

(b) Draw the smallest possible hexagon round it.

(c) What fraction of the hexagon is filled?

2 Here is a bigger regular hexagon.

(a) What is the largest number of small hexagons like this which can be fitted into it?

(b) What fraction of the hexagon is filled?

3 Find the number of small hexagons which can be fitted into hexagons of different sizes.

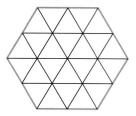

4 Copy and complete this table.

Size of hexagon	Fraction of hexagon filled
1	
2	$\frac{3}{4}$
3	
4	
5	
6	
7	
8	
9	
10	

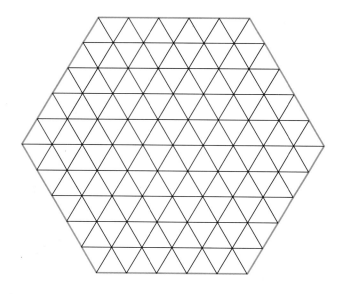

F33
page
187

5 How many small hexagons could you fit into a hexagon of size 30?

6 How many small hexagons could you fit into a hexagon of size N?

FITTING CIRCLES INTO CIRCLES

You might find square dot paper and isometric dot paper useful for this activity.

1 This picture shows two identical circles in a big circle.

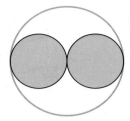

What percentage of the big circle is filled by the two circles?

2 Arrange three identical circles so that the circle they fit inside is as small as possible.

Make an accurate drawing of your arrangement. Measure the radii of your circles.

What percentage of the bigger circle is filled by the three circles?

3 Investigate how to arrange 4 identical circles so that they fit into the smallest possible circle. What about 5 circles? 6 circles? 7 circles? ...

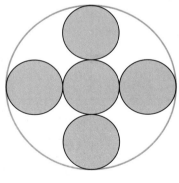

Is this the best arrangement for five circles?

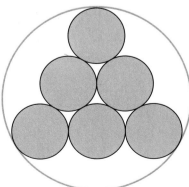

Is this the best arrangement for six circles?

F34
page
188

Find the percentage of the big circle filled with different arrangements of circles. You could do this by making accurate drawings and measuring. Or you could use Pythagoras' theorem and trigonometry.

FITTING SQUARES INTO A DIAGONAL SQUARE

1 Here are the first three patterns in a sequence where squares are fitted inside a diagonal square.

Pattern 1

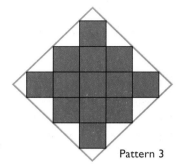

Pattern 2

Pattern 3

How many identical blue squares are there in each of these patterns?

2 Copy and complete this table. (You might find it easier to complete the second column last.)

Pattern number	Number of blue squares	Area of big square	Area of white in big square	Fraction of square filled
1				
2	5	8	3	0.625
3				
4				
5				
6				
7				
8				
9				
10				

3 (a) What is the area of white in the big square in the Nth pattern?

(b) What is the area of the big square in the Nth pattern?

(c) What is the number of blue squares in the Nth pattern?

(d) What fraction of the big square is filled by blue squares in the Nth pattern?

4 (a) Draw a graph to show the area of white in the big square in different patterns.

(b) Draw a graph to show the area of the big square in different patterns.

(c) Draw a graph to show the number of blue squares in different patterns.

(d) Draw a graph to show the fraction of the big square filled by blue squares in the Nth pattern.

You might want to use a graph plotter or a graphical calculator for this activity.

F33 page 187

F37 page 192

THE STRANGE CASE OF 5 SQUARES

You might find cardboard squares (ATM MATS or ATM generator tiles) useful for this activity.

F34
page
188

 I You have five cardboard squares. The problem is to arrange these squares so that they all fit into the smallest possible square without overlapping.

Here are several possible ways of arranging the five squares.

■ **1** Draw each of the arrangements of five squares in the box above. Draw a big square around each arrangement. Make the big square as small as possible.

■ **2** For each arrangement find the percentage of the big square which is filled by the five cardboard squares.

■ **3** Which arrangement would you use to fit the five squares into the smallest possible square without overlapping?

THE STRANGE CASE OF 85 SQUARES

 I If you have a number of cardboard squares and want to fit them into the smallest possible square without overlapping, the 'boring' arrangement is usually the best.

However, suppose you have 85 squares.

■ **1** A big square is drawn around each of the arrangements of 85 squares in the box above. If the big squares are made as small as possible, what percentage of each big square is filled by the 85 squares?

■ **2** Suppose you want to arrange other numbers of squares so that they fit into the smallest possible big square without overlapping.

What are the best arrangements for the following numbers of squares? What percentage of the big square is filled in each case?

(*a*) 80 squares   (*b*) 81 squares   (*c*) 82 squares   (*d*) 83 squares

(*e*) 84 squares   (*f*) 86 squares   (*g*) 87 squares

■ **3** Use the table you produced for question 2 of 'Fitting squares in a diagonal square' to find the next number which is 'like 85'.

 ■ **4** Now extend this table. You might want to use *Spread* to do this.

Use the extended table to find other numbers which are 'like 85'.

FITTING
SQUARES
INTO A
SLOPING
SQUARE

■ **1** Here are the first three patterns in a different sequence of patterns of squares.

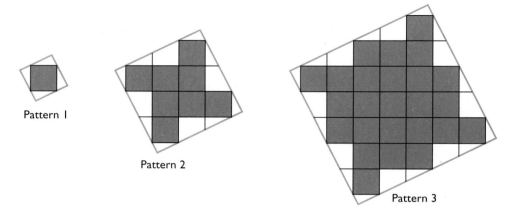

Pattern I

Pattern 2

Pattern 3

How many identical blue squares are there in each of these patterns?

■ **2** What is the area of the small white triangle at each of the corners of each pattern?

To answer this question you might find it helpful to look at this enlargement of the white square.

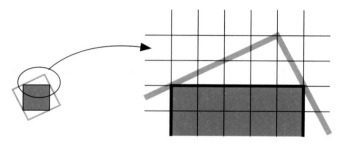

■ **3** Copy and complete this table.

Pattern number	Number of blue squares	Area of big square	Area of white in big square	Fraction of square filled
1				
2	8	12.8	4.8	0.625
3				
4				
5				
6				
7				
8				

■ **4** (*a*) What is the area of white in the big square in the *N*th pattern?

(*b*) What is the area of the big square in the *N*th pattern?

F34
page
188

(*c*) What is the number of blue squares in the *N*th pattern?

(*d*) What fraction of the big square is filled by blue squares in the *N*th pattern?

■ **5** What number is 'like 85' for sloping squares?

**PATTERNS
OF
TRIANGLES
AND
HEXAGONS**

1 Explore this sequence of patterns of triangles.

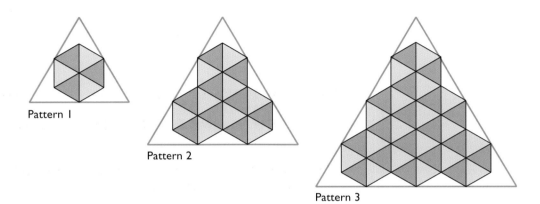

Pattern I

Pattern 2

Pattern 3

■ **2** Explore this sequence of patterns of hexagons.

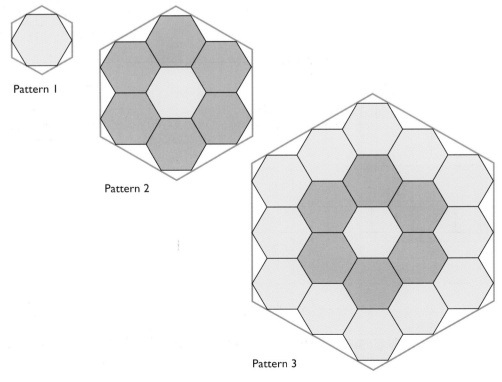

Pattern I

Pattern 2

Pattern 3

F33
page
187

17 WHAT IS THE SMALLEST?

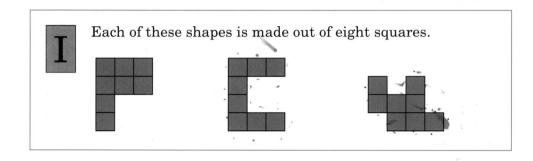

Each of these shapes is made out of eight squares.

You need squared paper for questions 1 to 3.

1 What is the perimeter of each of the shapes in the box above?

2 What is the smallest perimeter for a shape made of 8 squares?

3 What is the smallest perimeter for a shape made of 9 squares? 10 squares? 11 squares? 12 squares? ....

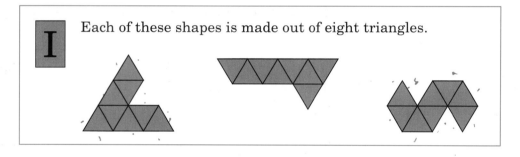

Each of these shapes is made out of eight triangles.

You need isometric paper for questions 4 to 6.

4 What is the perimeter of each of the shapes in the box above?

5 What is the smallest perimeter for a shape made of 8 triangles?

6 What is the smallest perimeter for a shape made of 9 triangles? 10 triangles? 11 triangles? 12 triangles? ....

You need hexagon paper or isometric dot paper for question 7.

7 What is the smallest perimeter for a shape made of 8 hexagons? 9 hexagons? 10 hexagons?

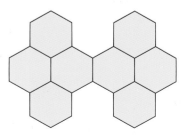

You need some pentagons for question 8.

8 What is the smallest perimeter for a shape made of 8 pentagons? 9 pentagons? 10 pentagons? ....

WHAT IS THE SMALLEST ANSWER?

 Here are two addition sums you can make using all of the digits 3, 4, 5, 6 and 7.

345 + 76
46 + 37 + 5

1 Which addition sum using all of the digits 3, 4, 5, 6 and 7 has the smallest answer?

 Here is a subtraction sum using the digits 3, 4, 5, 6 and 7.

765 – 43

2 Which subtraction sum using all of the digits 3, 4, 5, 6 and 7 has the smallest answer?

 Here is a multiplication sum using the digits 3, 4, 5, 6 and 7.

$34 \times 56 \times 7$

3 Which multiplication sum using all of the digits 3, 4, 5, 6 and 7 has the smallest answer?

 Here is a division sum using the digits 3, 4, 5, 6 and 7.

345 ÷ 67

4 Which division sum using all of the digits 3, 4, 5, 6 and 7 has the smallest answer?

WHAT IS THE SMALLEST NUMBER OF KEYSTROKES?

1 Imagine a calculator which only has these keys.

 This is how you might use this calculator to make the numbers 1 and 12.

 makes 1    makes 12

What keystrokes could you use to make the numbers 1, 2, 3, 4, 5, 6, ...?

Use the smallest number of keystrokes possible.

2 Imagine a calculator which has a different set of keys.

What keystrokes could you use in this calculator to make the numbers 1, 2, 3, 4, 5, 6, ...?

Use the smallest number of keystrokes possible.

F36
page
191

WHAT IS THE SMALLEST MULTIPLE?

For this activity you might find it helpful to get your calculator to count in 5s, or to count in 11s. And so on.

1 Write down four multiples of 5. What is the smallest multiple of 5 which ends in 0?

2 Write down four multiples of 11. What is the smallest multiple of 11 which does not have two digits the same?

3 What is the smallest multiple of 76 which is also a multiple of 38?

4 What is the smallest multiple of 23 with four digits?

5 What is the smallest multiple of 38 which ends in 7?

6 What is the smallest multiple of 4 which is also a multiple of 6?

7 What is the smallest multiple of 27 which ends in 25?

> **I** For questions 8 to 12 you might find it helpful to write numbers as a product of prime factors.
>
> For example: $10 = 2 \times 5$
> $12 = 2 \times 2 \times 3$
> $90 = 2 \times 3 \times 3 \times 5$

8 A number is a multiple of 6 and a multiple of 9. What is the smallest number it could be?

9 A number is a multiple of 40 and a multiple of 50. What is the smallest number it could be?

10 A number is a multiple of 12, a multiple of 16 and has three digits. What is the smallest number it could be?

11 A number is a multiple of 21 and 35 and has four digits. What is the smallest number it could be?

12 A number is a multiple of 12, a multiple of 16 and a multiple of 27. What is the smallest number it could be?

AN ODD NUMBER OF FACTORS

> **I** These are the factors of 81: 1, 3, 9, 27 and 81.
>
> So 81 has 5 factors.

1 What is the smallest number with exactly 3 factors?

2 What is the smallest number with exactly 5 factors?

3 What is the smallest number with exactly 7 factors? Exactly 9 factors? 11 factors? 13 factors? . . . .

F36
page
191

SMALLEST SURFACE AREA

1 This cuboid box has a volume of one litre.

Find a possible length, width and height for a cuboid with a volume of one litre. You might find it helpful to use *Spread* or a spreadsheet. Find the surface area of your cuboid.

Now find some more cuboids which have a volume of one litre. Find the surface area of each of your cuboids.

Which cuboid with a volume of one litre has the smallest surface area?

> **I** 1 litre = 1000 cm³

2

This cuboid box has a volume of half a litre.

Find a possible length, width and height for a cuboid with a volume of half a litre. You might find it helpful to use *Spread* or a spreadsheet. Find the surface area of your cuboid.

Now find some more cuboids which have a volume of half a litre. Find the surface area of each of your cuboids.

Which cuboid with a volume of half a litre has the smallest surface area?

3 The shape of a standard tin of beans is a cylinder with a diameter of 7.4 cm and a height of 10.8 cm.

What is the volume of this bean tin?

> **I** To find the volume of a bean tin (a cylinder) you multiply the area of the base of the cylinder by the height of the cylinder.

> **I** To find the area of the curved surface of the bean tin, imagine unwrapping the label, which is a rectangle.

What is the surface area of this bean tin?

Find the diameter and height of some other cylinders with the same volume. Calculate their surface areas.

Which cylinder with this volume has the smallest surface area?

> To find the volume of a Toblerone bar (a triangular prism) you multiply the area of the end by the length.

4 Find the volume and surface area of a Toblerone bar. The Toblerone bar has three edges of length 20.8 cm and six edges of length 3.6 cm.

Find the lengths of the edges and the surface areas of other equilateral triangular prisms with the same volume. Which equilateral triangular prism with this volume has the smallest surface area?

F34 page 188

SHORTEST ROUTES ON A CUBE AND A SPHERE

1 The edges of a hollow cube are each 8 cm long.

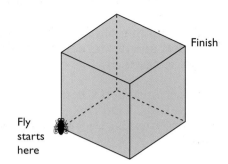

Finish

Fly starts here

A fly travels from one corner of the cube to the opposite corner.

What is the length of the shortest route the fly can take

(a) if it crawls only on edges?

(b) if it crawls anywhere on the surface of the cube?

(c) if it flies across the cube?

2 Answer question 1 for a journey from the middle of one face to the middle of the opposite face.

3 Answer question 1 for a journey from the middle of an edge to the middle of the opposite edge.

> You might find a net of the solid helpful for questions 1(b), 2(b), 3(b) and 4.

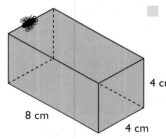

8 cm
4 cm
4 cm

4 A fly is in the middle of a short edge of this cuboid.

The fly crawls to the middle of the opposite edge using the shortest possible route.

(a) How many faces does it crawl across?

(b) What is the length of the journey?

5 Explore cuboids of different shapes. You could use these cuboids, or choose cuboids of your own.

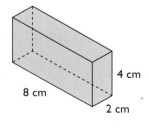

4 cm
8 cm
2 cm

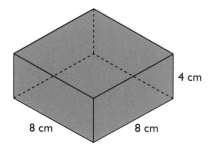

4 cm
8 cm
8 cm

Find the shortest route for a fly travelling from one point on the cuboid to another. You can choose the starting and finishing points. You can decide whether the fly is to crawl or to fly.

You might find it helpful to use nets for some of your exploration.

F35
page
190

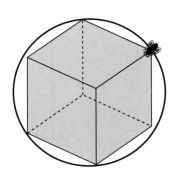

■ **6** A cube with edges of length 10 cm fits exactly into a sphere.

(*a*) What is the radius of the sphere?

A fly is sitting on the sphere at one vertex of the cube. It starts to crawl across the surface of the sphere. What is the length of its journey if:

(*b*) it takes the shortest route to the opposite vertex of the cube?

(*c*) it takes the shortest route to each of the other vertices of the cube?

SHORTEST ROUTES BETWEEN TOWNS

1 There are three towns A, B and C. They form an equilateral triangle. The distance between each pair of towns is 20 miles.

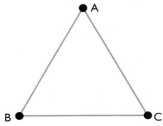

(*a*) Draw an accurate scale diagram showing the positions of the towns.

(*b*) A road network is to be built to link all three towns. The total length of the roads is to be as small as possible.

Experiment with different possible layouts for the roads to get the shortest network.

(*c*) Measure the angles between the roads in your shortest network.

2 There are three towns D, E and F. DF and EF are 26 miles and DE is 20 miles.

(*a*) Draw an accurate scale diagram showing the positions of the towns.

(*b*) Experiment to find out the shortest network for these three towns.

(*c*) Measure the angles between the roads in your shortest network.

3 Answer question 2 for three towns G, H and I where GH is 14 miles, HI is 16 miles and GI is 20 miles.

4 Answer question 2 for three towns J, K and L where JK is 15 miles, KL is 17 miles and JL is 31 miles.

C13 page 88

5 Answer question 2 for four towns M, N, O and P which form a square with a side length of 20 miles.

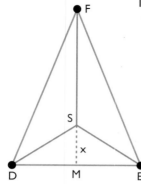

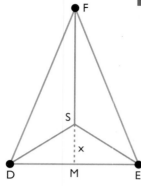

C18
page
93

6 Question 2 was about three towns which formed an isosceles triangle.

An isosceles triangle is symmetrical and therefore the shortest road network will be symmetrical too.

The only question is where the point S is on the line of symmetry.

Suppose the distance between S and the shortest side of the triangle is *x* miles.

(*a*) Use Pythagoras' theorem to calculate the length of the line of symmetry FM.

(*b*) Write down a formula for SF.

(*c*) Use Pythagoras' theorem to find a formula for the length of SD.

(*d*) Find a formula for SD + SE + SF.

(*e*) Use trial and improvement to find the value of *x* which makes the value of this formula as small as possible. You might want to use a graphical calculator or *Spread* for this.

(*f*) Use trigonometry to calculate the angle between DS and the line of symmetry.

(*g*) What are the angles between the three roads?

7 The shortest route system for question 5 looks something like this.

Use the method suggested in question 6 to find the exact positions of the points T and U. Find the angles between the roads.

A TIGHT FIT

1 (*a*) Draw this square on centimetre squared paper. What is the area of the square you have drawn?

Radius 2 cm

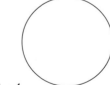

Radius 3 cm

Radius 4 cm

(*b*) Which of these circles will the square fit inside?

(*c*) What is the area of the smallest circle the square will fit into?

2 (*a*) If this rectangle is drawn on centimetre squared paper what is its area?

(*b*) What is the area of the smallest circle this rectangle will fit into?

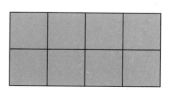

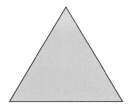

■ **3** 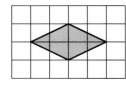 What is the area of the smallest circle this rhombus would fit into if it were copied onto squared paper?

■ **4** This equilateral triangle has sides of length 6 cm.

What is the area of the smallest circle this triangle will fit into?

■ **5** A square has sides of length 6 cm.

(*a*) Which of these spheres will it fit into?

The volume of a sphere with radius r is

$$\frac{4}{3}\pi r^3$$

Radius = 3 cm

Radius = 4 cm

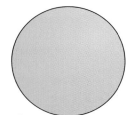
Radius = 5 cm

(*b*) What is the volume of the smallest sphere this square will fit into?

(*c*) What is the volume of the smallest cylinder this square will fit into?

(*d*) What is the volume of the smallest cube this square will fit into?

(*e*) What is the volume of the smallest cuboid this square will fit into?

■ **6** Find the smallest shape another shape will fit into.

You could start with one of these shapes, or with a shape of your own.

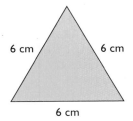
6 cm 6 cm
6 cm

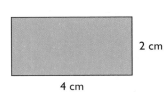
4 cm

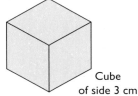
2 cm
Cube of side 3 cm

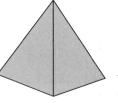
Tetrahedron of side 3 cm

Choose the type of solid you want your shape to fit into. It could be one of these.

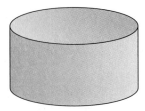

F34 page 188

Find the smallest possible volume for your solid container.

REVIEW EXERCISES F

EXERCISE 32 Probability 2

1 Someone spins an ordinary coin five times and happens to get five heads.

If they spin the coin again, what is the chance they will get a head for a sixth time?

2 (*a*) Some chocolate is left over from a class experiment. To decide who shall have the chocolate everyone in the class is given a number from 1 to 24. The winner is the person whose number is chosen.

The class decides to choose a number by opening a book, pointing to a word and counting how many letters the word has. Is this a fair way to decide who has won? If not, why not?

(*b*) Someone has a different idea. Four students are chosen. Each throws a dice. The four numbers they get are added.

Is this a fair way to choose who should have the chocolate? If not, why not?

3 Five students have their names written on the blackboard:

ANNE
JOHN
ANNETTE
JEAN
BEN

Letters are chosen at random. When a letter is chosen it is crossed off on the blackboard. If *N* is chosen all the *N*s on the blackboard are crossed off.

The winner is the person whose name is crossed off first.

(*a*) Which of the five students are most likely to win?

(*b*) Which of the five students cannot be outright winners?

4 You throw two dice.

(*a*) What is the probability of getting two sixes?

(*b*) What is the probability of getting a five and a four?

5 Class 9A has 30 students, 18 of whom are girls. Class 9B has 25 students 10 of whom are girls.

(*a*) A student is picked at random from class 9A. What is the probability that this student is a girl?

(*b*) What is the probability that a student picked at random from class 9B is a girl?

You could use a tree diagram to help answer part (*c*).

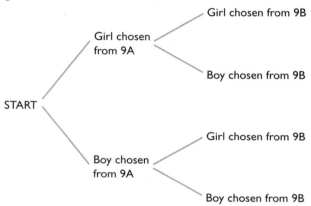

(*c*) Two students are picked at random, one from class 9A and one from class 9B. What is the probability that they are both girls? What is the probability that one is a girl and one is a boy?

6 A normal set of dominoes contains 28 dominoes, all possible pairs of numbers from (0, 0) to (6, 6).

A domino is picked at random from a set.

(*a*) What is the probability of getting a domino with a 5?

(*b*) What is the probability of getting a domino with a 4?

(*c*) What is the probability of getting a domino with a 5 and a 4?

7 You might find a tree diagram helpful to answer this question.

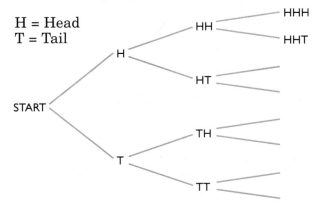

H = Head
T = Tail

You throw three coins.

(a) What is the probability of getting three heads?

(b) What is the probability of getting two heads and a tail?

(c) What is the probability of getting three tails?

8 You are dealt three cards from a well shuffled pack.

(a) What is the probability that they are all hearts?

(b) What is the probability that they are the ace, the king and the queen of hearts?

9 Some people have PIN numbers. PIN numbers are secret to you. You type in your PIN number when you use a cashcard in a bank cash machine, for example.

PIN numbers usually have four digits.

Here are some PIN numbers:

1325   2469   3132   4287   6366

Choose one of these PIN numbers. Suppose four dice are thrown.

(a) How likely is it that the four numbers shown on the dice will be the digits of the PIN number you have chosen?

(b) Why does your answer depend on which PIN number you chose?

EXERCISE 33 Number Sequences

1 (a) Find the next two terms of each of these sequences:

    (i)   4, 8, 12, 16, 20, 24, ...
    (ii) 1, 4, 7, 10, 13, 16, ...
    (iii) 10, 30, 50, 70, 90, 110, ...
    (iv) 6, 19, 32, 45, 58, 71, 84, ...
    (v) 50, 45, 40, 35, 30, 25, ...

  (b) Explain the rule for finding the next term of each sequence.

  (c) Find the 20th term of each sequence.

  (d) Find a formula for the Nth term of each sequence.

2 (a) Find the next two terms of each of these sequences:

    (i)   1, 3, 7, 13, 21, 31, ...
    (ii) 25, 24, 22, 19, 15, 10, ...
    (iii) 1, 4, 9, 16, 25, 36, 49, ...
    (iv) 0, 3, 8, 15, 24, 35, 48, ...
    (v) 2, 8, 18, 32, 50, 72, 98, ...

  (b) Explain the rule for finding the next term of each sequence.

  (c) Find the 20th term of sequences (iii), (iv) and (v).

  (d) Find a formula for the Nth term of sequences (iii), (iv) and (v).

3 (a) Find the next two terms of each of these sequences:

    (i)   5, 10, 20, 40, 80, 160, ...
    (ii) 800, 400, 200, 100, 50, 25, ...
    (iii) 3, −6, 12, −24, 48, −96, ...
    (iv) −2, 6, −18, 54, −162, 486, ...
    (v) 32, 48, 56, 60, 62, 63, ...
    (vi) 271, 514, 676, 784, 856, 904, ...

  (b) Explain the rule for finding the next term of each sequence.

  (c) Find the 15th term of each sequence.

  (d) What happens to each sequence eventually?

4 Here is a sequence:

5, 12, 21, 32, 45, 60, ...

(a) Write down the next three terms of this sequence.

(b) Explain the rule for finding the next term of this sequence.

(c) Factorise the 3rd term of this sequence into prime factors.

(d) Factorise the 7th term of this sequence into prime factors.

(e) Factorise the 13th term of this sequence into prime factors.

(f) What is the 40th term of this sequence?

(g) What is the Nth term of this sequence?

(h) How many of the numbers in this sequence are prime numbers?

EXERCISE 34 Area and Volume

1 Find the volumes of these cuboids.

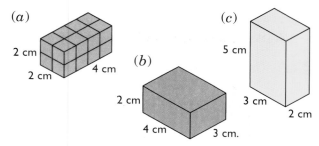

(a) 2 cm, 2 cm, 4 cm

(b) 2 cm, 4 cm, 3 cm.

(c) 5 cm, 3 cm, 2 cm

2 Find the surface areas of the cuboids in question 1.

3 Here is a picture of a cereal packet.

The length of the packet is 20.3 cm, the width is 5.8 cm and the height is 28.5 cm.

(a) Find the volume of the packet.

(b) Find the surface area of the packet.

> To find the **volume of a cylinder**, you **multiply the area of its base (a circle) by its height**.
>
> To find the **surface area of a cylinder**, you **add the area of the top, the area of the bottom and the area of the curved side**. To find the **area of the curved side, flatten it into a rectangle.**

4 A cylinder has a radius of 3 cm and a length of 8 cm.

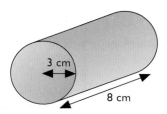

3 cm

8 cm

(a) Find the volume of the cylinder.

(b) Find the surface area of the cylinder.

5 Here is a drum of custard powder.

The diameter of the drum is 8.7 cm and its height is 9.2 cm.

(a) Find the volume of the drum.

(b) Find the surface area of the drum.

6 (a) Find the volume and the area of the curved surface of this cylinder.

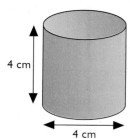

4 cm

4 cm

(b) Find the volume and surface area of this sphere. Compare the surface area of this sphere with the area of the curved surface of the cylinder.

Radius 2 cm

(c) The cylinder in (a) fits exactly round the sphere in (b).

Describe the cylinder which fits exactly around the sphere below.

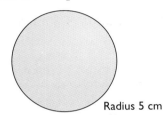

Radius 5 cm

What is the surface area of this sphere and the area of the curved surface of this cylinder?

(A sphere with radius r has volume $\frac{4}{3}\pi r^3$ and surface area $4\pi r^2$)

■ 7 Find the volume and surface area of this hemisphere.

Radius 6 cm

■ 8 Find the area of this triangle.

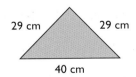

29 cm   29 cm
40 cm

This triangle is the cross-section of a triangular prism of length 30 cm.

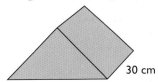

30 cm

Find the volume and surface area of the prism.

■ 9

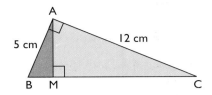

A
5 cm   12 cm
B   M   C

(a) Find the area of the large triangle, which is coloured red and blue.

(b) Find the length of BC.

(c) Find the length of the line AM.

(d) FInd the ratio of red to blue in the large triangle.

■ 10 Here is a picture of a warning sign.

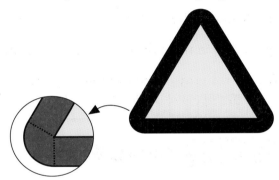

The band is 3 cm wide and the yellow equilateral triangle has sides of length 50 cm.

Find the total area of the black band.

■ 11

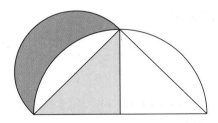

The picture above consists of straight lines and two semicircles.

The radius of the larger semicircle is 8 cm.

(a) Find the blue area and the red area.

(b) Which of the two areas is bigger?

(c) How sure are you about your answer to part (b)? Does it depend on the accuracy of the numbers on your calculator?

12 In the picture the largest semicircle has a radius of 10 cm and the two smallest semicircles have a radius of 2 cm.

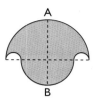

(a) What is the orange area?

(b) What is the area of the circle with AB as one of its diameters?

(c) Which of your answers to parts (a) and (b) is bigger?

(d) What happens if the radius of the two smallest semicircles is 3 cm instead of 2 cm?

EXERCISE 35 3-D Geometry

1 Draw a sketch of a net for this cuboid.

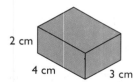

2 cm
4 cm
3 cm

2 Here is an isometric drawing for a model made of four interlocking cubes.

Make as many different models from four interlocking cubes as you can.

Draw an isometric drawing for each of your models.

3 Here is an isometric drawing for a model made of six cubes.

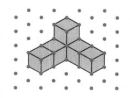

What is the surface area of the model?

4 (a) Orange paint is splodged on one corner of a cube.

    (i) How many edges have orange paint at one end?

    (ii) How many faces have orange paint at one corner?

(b) Orange paint is now splodged on a second corner as well. One edge has paint at both ends.

    (i) How many edges now have orange paint at one end?

    (ii) How many faces now have orange paint at one corner? At two corners?

(c) Orange paint is now splodged on a third corner. One face now has paint at three of its corners.

What about the faces and edges of the cube now?

5

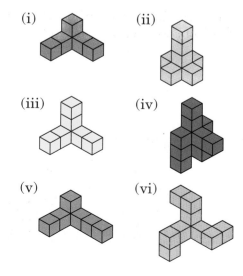

Use this tree with the following models:

(i)   (ii)

(iii)   (iv)

(v)   (vi)

Which models are labelled A?

Which models are labelled B?

Which models are labelled C?

Which models are labelled D?

■ **6** Triangles are made by joining three corners of a cube.

How many different shapes can the triangles have?

Draw sketches of the possible shapes.

EXERCISE 36 Properties of Numbers 2

1 Put a number in your calculator. Add 273. What do you have to do to the answer to get back to the starting number?

2 Put a number in your calculator. Multiply by 13. What do you have to do to the answer to get back to the starting number?

3 (*a*) What is the largest multiple of 2 you can make from the digits 2, 3 and 4?

(*b*) What is the largest multiple of 3 you can make from the digits 3, 4 and 5?

(*c*) What is the largest multiple of 4 you can make from the digits 4, 5 and 6?

(*d*) What is the largest multiple of 5 you can make from the digits 5, 6 and 7?

(*e*) What is the largest multiple of 6 you can make from the digits 6, 7 and 8?

(*f*) What is the largest multiple of 7 you can make from the digits 7, 8 and 9?

4

Use this tree with the numbers 20, 21, ... 30.

Which numbered are labelled A?

Which are labelled B?

Which are labelled C?

Which are labelled D?

Which are labelled E?

5 (*a*) Which prime numbers are factors of 42?

(*b*) Which prime numbers are factors of 54?

(*c*) Which prime numbers are factors of both 42 and 54?

(*d*) What is the biggest number which is a factor of both 42 and 54?

■ **6** This is how the number 18 can be written as the product of prime factors:

18 = 2 x 3 x 3

(*a*) Write these numbers as the product of prime factors

(i) 12 (ii) 15 (iii) 21 (iv) 24 (v) 27

(*b*) (i) List the factors of 50.

(ii) How many factors does 50 have?

(iii) Write 50 as the product of prime factors.

(*c*) (i) List the factors of 45.

(ii) How many factors does 45 have?

(iii) Write 45 as the product of prime factors.

(*d*) Find a number bigger than 50 which has the same number of factors as 50.

■ **7** Put a number in your calculator. Cube the number. What do you have to do to the answer to get back to the starting number?

■ **8** Put a number in your calculator. Find the square root of the number. What do you have to do to get back to the starting number? Explain why it will usually not be possible to get back *exactly* to the starting number using the calculator.

EXERCISE 37 Using Graphs of Functions

1 The perimeter of this rectangle is 20 cm.

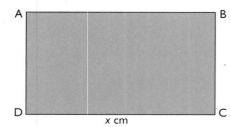

A   B

D   C

x cm

(a) What is the length of side BC in terms of *x*?

(b) If the area of the rectangle is A cm² write down a formula for A in terms of *x*.

(c) Copy and complete this table.

x	2	3	4	5	6	7	8
A		21					16

(d) Draw a graph of A plotted against *x*.

(e) Find from your graph the largest area this rectangle can have.

(f) What shape is the rectangle for this area?

2 The area of the rectangle is 36 cm².

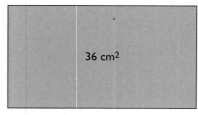

36 cm²

x cm

The perimeter of the rectangle is *p* cm.

(a) Find a formula for *p* in terms of *x*.

(b) Copy and complete this table.

x	3	4	5	6	7	8	9	10
p	30				25			

(c) Draw a graph of *p* plotted against *x*.

(d) Find from your graph the smallest perimeter this rectangle could have.

(e) What shape is the rectangle for this perimeter?

3 Answer question 2 for a rectangle with an area of 24 cm².

4 A rectangular enclosure is made against a wall from a piece of fencing 60 metres long.

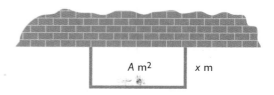

A m²   *x* m

(a) Find a formula for the area A m² of the enclosure in terms of *x*.

(b) Draw a graph of A plotted against *x*.

(c) What is the largest area the enclosure can be?

5 An arrangement of roads is to be built linking four towns, A, B, C and D.

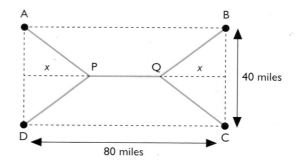

A   B

x P   Q *x*   40 miles

D   C

80 miles

(a) Find the length PQ in terms of *x*.

(b) Find the length AP in terms of *x*.

(c) Find the formula for the total length L of the road network in terms of *x*.

(d) Plot a graph of L against *x*.

(e) Find the minimum length of the road network.